"Bouter En Avant!"

FULL STEAM AHEAD

with

JULIA CHILD

a *mémoire* of friendship

Madeleine de Jean

TELEMACHUS PRESS

This book is a work of fiction. Names, characters, places and incidents are either the product of the author's imagination or are used fictitiously. Any resemblance to actual persons, living or dead, or to actual events or locales is entirely coincidental.

The publisher does not have any control over and does not assume any responsibility for author or third-party websites or their content.

Cover design by Telemachus Press, LLC

Cover art by Johnny Breeze, Steve Himes of Telemachus Press, LLC based on the iconic photograph by Bonnie Schiffman: Julia and the Big Fouet

Published by Telemachus Press, LLC
http://www.telemachuspress.com

Visit the author website:
http://www.madeleinedeJean.com

Or read the Madeleine's blog:
http://champagnetoujours.blogspot.com

ISBN: 978-1-941536-37-7 (eBook)
ISBN: 978-1-941536-38-4 (paperback)

Version 2014.09.17

Printed in the United States of America

10 9 8 7 6 5 4 3 2 1

TABLE OF CONTENTS

PROLOGUE

As I travel the remembered meals, wines, streets and venues, of my friendship with Julia Child each one shimmers as though it is about to re-appear, calling clear, as heard as on the very days and evenings we shared them with laughter and bubbly *'carillon'*—"bells of friendship"—toasts ringing. There are even conversations of heartfelt distress and sometimes of dreams ending which too remain tangible. In all such moments we knew we were sisters under the skin just separated in time-warps: as instinct told her that my zany sense of humor allied with hers, she also knew that her—not often expressed—sadnesses were by me compassionately understood, as I understood mine were by Julia. What I offer here in this *mémoire* of a friendship does not betray any secret treasures—whether of gold or of bronze—not meant for others. Sisters to the end.

What I do serve to you, so you can savor more clearly the truly unique soul Julia possessed, is of generosity to friends, of wishing well to all—especially to those inclined to gastronomic principles and classical sauce and to fine wines—, of her pure delight in being delighted, of reveling in eccentricities, of pleasure in gabbing with intelligence about everything.

Intelligence; Curiosity: these were Julia hallmarks. She was curious about it all, whatever form or size, dimension or aesthetic: Julia wanted to know more. As important as the *Plat Principal* of Julia herself, was her generous serving of laughter sauced with kindness.

Julia spoke a special language. Of course most of the western world recognizes her voice because of her distinctive Julia-fluting timbre and pronunciation. But, just as once she had gained total control of the principals behind French classical cuisine, with her sense of play and imagination she could take dishes into special realms, dedicating an evening's repast to the guest of honor by painting with spices, or, at her large *'piano'*, playing an allegretto on the sauce; she also, once she had command of spoken French, could, having fun with WWII 'Franglais' terms, create new meanings which were quite simply, *Julia!*

"*BOUTER EN AVANT!*" was Julia's rallying cry upon which I often saw her sally forth full of energy and zest for the game about to begin. Julia translated these words to mean, "Boots on the Ground; Full Steam Ahead!" Actually the phrase is a special Julia concoction, a wordy dish from a mediaeval revolutionary French family, making it uniquely hers. A real Julia *'Wowza!'*

Julia frequently said that as soon as she was off television, within a few months no one would remember who she was. Well, Julia, your millions and millions of fans definitely disagree with you solely on that one. So I dedicate this story of Julia to all her devotees, admirers and followers, who remain untiringly committed to remembering and celebrating the remarkable woman she was, whether actively by imitating her in the buttery kitchen of high standards, or by cheering her on while watching and learning from her television reruns, or by delving into her cookbooks, or by simply having more gastronomic and vinous fun. To all of you, *Bon Appétit!*

Last night, in dreams, I went back to Aspen, and Julia was there fluting, "Welcome, *chers amis; bienvenue à tous,* and, waving her large *fouet,* she stirred up quite a wind gathering us all together to watch her create and to taste her latest dish.

So, let's Full Speed Ahead with our dear friend, Julia Child.

Bouter en Avant!

Chapter 1
Julia's Last Letter

Tuesday, August 17, 2004 was like most days in August in Palm Springs: hot; hotter; melt-down.

In the brilliant glare, notwithstanding a wide-brimmed straw hat, I dragged while crossing the empty parking lot to the Post Office. Inside, my lone footsteps echoed, hollowly reverberating.

"One-twenty in the shade; and risin'," my brain heard Johnny Cash's up-note.

Yet I was down. So, I tried humming and that made me feel cooler while I collected my mail.

Despite, my spirit kept registering 'Empty'.

Listlessly I riffled through the bunch. A disturbed post card flew out growing wings, sailing past to cartwheel across the terrazzo floor. I stooped; my fingers touched it; then a sudden freeze descended: I could not breathe. "A joke," I gasped and grasped the truant. "You're announcing some crazy joke!" I held it up and shook it, not knowing if I should cry or laugh. "She's written to say 'it's all been *tout simplement une plaisanterie*'." Tears flooded my eyes. Through swimming vision, looking back at me from the front of the card, in bright red was the familiar logo of a *batterie de cuisine* and the words "from Julia Child's Kitchen." Turning it over I was staring at Julia's handwriting, and could hear her warbling the words, thanking me for early birthday wishes, asking when we would meet again. *Meet* again! "Why did I listen to Stephanie," I blurted, "Oh Stephanie, how, why did you do it?" A large, salty one rolled down to my lips. Stephanie and Julia were playing a joke on me. *Certainement.* What else could it be? For in my hand I was holding a card with Stephanie's boss's unmistakable flourishing "Julia" followed by a heart. I danced out into the still-empty parking lot, no longer feeling the waves of heat. A big joke!

I turned the card over again. Proof my friend Julia Child was playing a joke: It had been mailed four days earlier on August 13.

August 13, 2004.

The pre-dawn dark of August 13 already was presaging the heat of the day to come as I nestled a magnum of 1979 *Rosé* Champagne deep into ice in a chest in my car. This Friday the 13th was a perfect day to get out of dodge. At 4:30 AM the heat promised another brutal day in the California desert: Far better to be in Santa Barbara where ocean breezes keep temperatures moderate.

And Julia loved surprises.

I had a free day on my calendar and was taking it to regale this dear friend I'd not seen in too long. As I crossed the front lawn back to the house I looked into the sky. Stars would soon be overcome by an orange glow still tiptoeing in in the distant east.

I went into the house to leave a voice-message at The Ivy Restaurant in Los Angeles saying I'd be there around 7:45. Before Santa Barbara I was driving to The Ivy to pick up one of their addictive, sinfully rich chocolate cakes. My friend's birthday was in two days and she loved chocolate, almost as much as she loved butter, *Rosé* Champagne, and surprises. Recently, while she was in a nursing facility overcoming a bad reaction to a knee-implant, I fed her craving by sending two ten-pound bars of Scharffen Berger chocolate. When we next spoke she warbled how she'd eaten them both "all by myself!" Well, maybe she'd given a morsel to Stephanie? Or to her doctor?

Finished inside the house, I picked up my keys and opened the front door.

Then the house phone rang. *"Zut."* Normally I would keep going, but a call before dawn? My daughter! I raced to catch it before the machine. "Hello?"

"Madeleine." It was not a question.

And it was not my daughter. "Stephanie? Stephanie? How did you know I'm on my way?"

Only silence followed, punctuated by a loud question mark from her side.

I raced on: "The Champagne's in ice. I'm about to leave, coming with her favorite *Rosé* and a chocolate cake from The Ivy. Oh, Stephanie, it's a surprise. Don't tell her. How did *you* know?"

Some fifteen years before, with her new degree in Cuisine from the prestigious Culinary Institute of America and a newer one in office management from Katherine Gibbs in Boston, Stephanie Hersh got her dream job working for Julia Child. She became Julia's Executive Assistant and office and household *Johanna Factotum*, doing everything Julia needed from running the office, to preparing meals and overseeing the Cambridge household. Over those years Julia's office needs expanded into an international empire of television shows and personal appearances. Stephanie normally had her capable hands very full.

Julia progressed more and more into staying longer and longer in Santa Barbara, California, delaying her return to Cambridge, Massachusetts. Especially after the long illness and death of Julia's beloved soul-mate-husband, Paul, she and Stephanie found it necessary for Stephanie to come more frequently to Santa Barbara. Finally Stephanie packed up and moved to the Pacific Coast. So I knew she was calling from where it also was 4:45 in the morning, and only two days before Julia's 92nd birthday.

"Madeleine." Still she hesitated. Hesitancy is not like Stephanie, and my alert-mode switched on. "Julia. Julia, Madeleine," quietly she talked, her voice almost betraying her beginning grief. "I walked in and found her. Just now. In bed. Her new kitty at her side."

I know I said I was coming; now coming to help *her*. But she knew what she had to do, and declined the offer. Stephanie is a great manager. And that day she knew she had much to manage all around the world. The woman for whom she'd worked with so well for fifteen years was an International Star.

So I called The Ivy and explained to just-arrived owner Richard Irving why I would not be coming. Then I went back outside into the beginning day and took Julia's magnum of Champagne out of the ice. The rest of that Friday, August 13, I listened to the continuous media coverage celebrating Julia, her life's work saving America from death-by-frozen-TV-dinners, playing and repeating the Saturday Night Live spoof on blood gushing from her cut finger, the replays of her first black and white shows from the 1960s, the shows that would catapult her into the *fouet*-wielding goddess of America's kitchens, making her voice as well-known as that of the Queen. In fact we crowned her our culinary Queen; her kingdom the kitchens and dining tables of the world; her unmistakable *"Bon Appétit!"* tirelessly imitated and tirelessly heard.

So, four mornings later, on August 17, 2004, in the Post Office, when I picked up that familiar card with her familiar handwritten "Julia" with a heart, my heart did skip a beat and my brain went into dreaming away this sadness of this, her last letter, as instead an announcement of some silly, and not-like-her joke.

Chapter 2
America's *Marianne Marseillaise*

E.Delacroix: Le 28 Juillet; la Liberté, *Musée de Louvre*
Extraction from Julia Child and Big Fouet photo by Bonnie Schiffman

Maybe we choose for friends those who remind us of home?

Sixteen years before, in 1988 after Julia and I first met, we enjoyed chatty sessions over sherry or lunch at her Santa Barbara condo, or here over dinner at my house, or over lunch at *Le Dôme* in Los Angeles, or after an event we'd participated in somewhere, during which we discovered that for both of us 'home' was synonymous with France; culture, traditions, literature, theatre, places, aromas, meals. Gabbing and crossing each other's words we'd talk about our favorite moments and places in Paris, like when at Poilane's bakery in the *Croix Rouge*—only months apart in 1970—, we'd both ogled *Chef-Boulanger* Poilane's gorgeously sweat-glistened and scantily clad muscle men who stoked those basement ovens to Hades-sweaty temperatures; or when we'd—surprisingly some twenty years apart—visited the *same* famous Milliner on *rue de la Paix*—each harboring a secret desire to try our hand at designing; or savoring the remembered tastes of the **that** *omelette* or, **the** *socca* or **superb** *filet de sole,* or (yummy) *pommes paille,* or *soufflé* made supremely at this or that Paris, or Marseilles, or Nice, restaurant on this or that corner, served by the *same* waiter; or, then, when our paths had almost collided in 1964 there or there in Cambridge, Massachusetts, which was home to us both in 1964. In one gab session we discovered that theatre-loving Julia and Paul had seen me in a production of *Edward II* at Harvard's Loeb theatre that year. And that they had attended the production with their cherished friend, the *'marraine'*—'godmother'—of *Mastering the Art of French Cooking,* Avis de Voto, who was in 1964 Assistant to the Dean of Students at Radcliffe, for whom I also worked. Six or five or two degrees of separation?

Once, during such a memory-lane session here at my house, when I told Julia about Radcliffe College's Briggs Hall's 'Julia Child Aficionados', Julia smacked the table and exclaimed in her most Julia voice, *"Flûte!* We should have met then! Oh..." She stopped. She paused. And, with that Julia-goddess-mother-of-us-all wise look, looked at me and laughed, "That's silly; we are friends *now.*"

1964: Indeed Julia and I could have met in 1964, forty years before, and not just sixteen. There were many opportunities. As a young woman in Cambridge, Massachusetts, often I did almost run smack into Julia; like when she came into 'Design Research' (dubbed by me 'Divine Research' because of extravagant prices according to a Harvard-teaching-fellow's wife) shopping for the large white plates she would use on those first black-and-white TV programs; or side-by-side at Savenor's counter picking up the Christmas birds from Jack. After a while she seemed to recognize me and would smile as though she thought we did know each other. Yes, *flûte!*, too bad I was too shy to say hello and tell her how much of a role she was playing in my life, and in that of several of

Radcliffe's Briggs Hall residents, blooming Julia-Child-*Gourmettes. Défense de cracher!*

And *this* is one of my stories over which Julia would put up her feet figuratively and sit back. She liked hearing it because it told of how her life's work began to interact with and transform mine and some Radcliffe students' as well.

That afternoon I first told it was in 1990, and Julia was visiting with me. While we enjoyed a cup of tea and a glass of Sandeman's Amontillado, I began. Julia took a few toasted almonds, sipped her sherry and sat back to listen:

'Briggs Hall', not far across Cambridge from where Julia and Paul lived, was one of Radcliffe's residential 'dormitories', and was where I, a young married, just-childed woman, lived with my family in 1964. Briggs Hall was where I worked.

Radcliffe College titled me Briggs Hall's "Senior Resident" because the Dean of Women, Kathleen Elliot, was making changes in the long-honored system of older women directing the flair and welfare of college girls' dormitories. To preside over Radcliffe's resident halls Mrs. Elliot now decided to install young women, most with families, believing that being close in age and in sensibilities to the students, we would give a somewhat normal sensitivity to the often traumatic, frequently emotional college years. Her main goal was to make sure that every girl accepted to Radcliffe graduated and as happily as possible.

The year I stepped into that position at Briggs Hall was 1964.

And in 1964 Julia was vibrating black-and-white television, leading a peaceful revolution, like a new world '*Marianne Marseillaise*', who, with her large *fouet* was calling us to action.

Eugène Delacroix: Le 28 Juillet; la Liberté guidant le people, Musée de Louvre
Julia Child and the Big Fouet photo by Bonnie Schiffman

1964. What was life like in America in 1964? Well …

On that 1990 afternoon Julia sat forward and joined in this reminiscing, adding great stuff to the list.

For one, in 1964 you could still cross 5th Avenue in New York City in a leisurely fashion.

And Yellow Taxi drivers took passengers swiftly to their destinations without aggressive gestures or international expletives.

On Rodeo Drive on the West Coast, Rolls Royces rolled at the 10 mph limit giving occupants time to choose which glamorous shops to spend in.

And back in Boston a city bus could cross the Charles River from Cambridge and get passengers to downtown in a quarter of an hour. There were far fewer of us in 1964.

Though it was *de rigueur* for 'gentlemen' to wear hats and 'ladies' to add gloves to their ensembles when they left the house, the world was opening up for Americans in 1964.

Music clubs in New York and New Orleans and Los Angeles were jumping and surfing with Beatles and Beach Boys, Connie Francis and The Lancasters, going into new worlds with Bob Dylan, Judy Collins and Jacques Brel, with Dionne Warwick and The Supremes.

And in 1964 black and white televisions were in almost every American house. Those bulky tiny-screen-sets were turned on each evening for the news of the world buoyed by fantastic commercials, all attended in full starched and polished dress like a mandatory ritual by most American families.

While those families followed the custom shown in their favorite TV show, Ozzie and Harriet, by dressing for dinner with fresh shirts and creased trousers, belted plaid skirts and fluffy hair-dos, the dining table itself was giving place, in 1964, to individual TV-tables. One of the most popular commercials that families watched told American housewives how they could have more leisure time to themselves for beautifying with home permanents and for card-playing with friends, how this time out of the kitchen could be had by purchasing the newest, the hottest, the best, frozen dinners. No longer did Mrs. America have to slave at a hot stove. She merely put on her little "Bewitched" apron, wiggled her nose, and, imitating the commercial instructions, heated up aluminum foil covered frozen containers. Soon most families nightly pulled up TV-side with TV-tables set with bubbling hot TV-dinners. And the "little lady", stress-free and beautifully coiffed could listen with the family to the nightly news or The Ed Sullivan Show introducing the Beatles or The Supremes. Sure those meals tasted like cardboard with sides of paste, but who cared? Stress-less dining was the newest and latest and was uniquely American. The family felt liberated.

"And the kitchen was always clean," Julia trilled.

America was on top of the world in 1964. John Glenn, Scott Carpenter and Gordon Cooper had orbited the earth telling us about four sunrises in a single orbit and the beauties of the Atlas Mountains and the Rockies, which we could hear broadcast over satellite transmission from across the Atlantic if necessary.

Our 1964 dollar was also soaring. More and more Americans, students, business people, and whole families, crossed the Atlantic to see Europe on gorgeous trans-Atlantic liners at dirt-cheap prices. There they found the cost of a fine two-course lunch, with a glass of decent wine, in London, was three shillings six pence, equivalent to .55 cents. In France a bottle of Château Haut Brion 1945, one of the greatest years in Bordeaux history and from the oldest of one of the reigning top five Chateaux, could be purchased for ten dollars.

"'Europe on Five Dollar a Day'," Julia added to the list.

All these wonders and so much time to enjoy them were generally believed to have a connection to such wonders as frozen TV dinners.

However, in 1964, in Cambridge, Massachusetts, at Radcliffe College things were starting to percolate on both sides of this Revolution.

Early in 1964 Radcliffe's Dean Kathleen Elliot, wasted no time implementing her momentous decision to install young "Senior Residents", replacing older "House Mothers", in her women's residential halls.

Though Radcliffe students were cutting-edge forward-thinking, enough was quite enough thought *some*. Such a change at the helm of Briggs Hall, the most tradition-bound of Radcliffe's six women's residences, was not so welcome, causing concern that this was instead a flag signaling the end of long-held annual events, loved traditions.

For years Briggs Hall had been presided over by an older woman who esteemed and maintained formal lifestyles and traditions, considered in other, more forward-looking Radcliffe halls as better by-gone.

Chief among these formalities was the nightly procession into dinner from the living room to the dining room. (Not unlike, in many scholarly and fancifully-minded minds, the Bourbon Kings process to dinner, where perhaps on a good evening one might witness the King lop off the top of an egg?) At Briggs Hall, every evening the dinner hour was announced by bells. And, to duo-piano Mozart provided by fellow residents, Briggs's girls gathered in the formal living room by the fireplaces and waited for their House Mother's arrival. No one entered the dining room before she did.

Next, Wednesday nights marked another Briggs dining tradition. Preceding dinner, in the living room, from silver trays, sherry was served.

Wednesday night was Guest Night and Briggs Hall ladies invited guests to dine. Sometimes a Harvard professor was invited by a group of students; more often a favorite friend from Harvard was tapped; or sometimes a parent in town was a guest. After the glass of sherry, the Lady of the House led her Briggs Hall ladies and their guests into the dining room.

These dinner traditions were particular favorites of the dining room manager, Grace. Grace loved to see her domain set with starched white tablecloths and napkins, shined silverware and sparkling glassware. Grace and her uniformed Assistants served formally and were proud of the traditions they upheld for Radcliffe College. Dining graciously was one of life's treasures to be passed along. And Grace was gracious dining's head Muse. Grace had—thankfully—never tasted a frozen TV-dinner. (Julia chortled.)

Another tradition maintained at Briggs Hall was Sunday afternoon High Tea, again served in the living room. While on every day during the week if any Briggs Hall resident desired a cup of tea in the late afternoon, they could find one in the dining room where Grace had tea ready for her girls. But Sunday's Tea was High, and there were small sandwiches and pastries and guests (meaning Harvard Men) were allowed. The samovar sparkled and hissed, and Grace bustled about making sure.

There was always a Christmas-Holiday tree ceremony. Singing and piano playing and perhaps barrel-aged cider, were expected accompaniments.

Springtime brought a series of Strawberry Breakfasts held before the end of the term, which were quite formal occasions too.

So while most of Radcliffe's Residential Halls had by 1964 voted out these traditions, before her departure the last House Mother of Briggs Hall and the Dean of Women invited all residents down into the living room where, over a glass of sherry and a biscuit, a vote was held. Did they wish to continue, after her departure, these more formal occasions? Or would they prefer to enter the casual modern age? Overwhelmingly Briggs Hall women voted to continue the ways of tradition.

"They all revolved around intelligent conversation stimulated by dining," justified Julia chirruped.

And in 1964 I was asked to come to meet the Dean of Women at Radcliff. At my first meeting with Kathleen Elliot, in her gorgeously windowed office, the students' desires were explained to me. Coming from a formal boarding school experience where students still curtsied to the Reverend Mother; coming from schooling in London, during which time I was presented to the Queen Mother, I was not shy of Briggs Hall's traditions: instead, I thought them the way things were done. (Digesting this, Julia savored some sherry and smacked her lips approvingly.) So, in 1964 I became the first "Senior Resident" of Briggs Hall, where the residents mandated and I maintained gastronomic and social formalities. (Could Julia have wished for anything less in a friend?)

And in 1964, across the Charles River from Briggs Hall, this remarkable woman, Julia Child, like a pacific *Marseillaise*, was blazing forth onto Boston's Television's stage. In "The French Chef" she was proposing a big return to culinary tradition by warbling America back into the kitchen. Like a fairy-god-mother she conjured up an odd thing she trillingly called "*fouet*" with which she beat eggs by hand into clouds, and, blithely tossing out the cake-mix, actually made cakes and meringues and, dismissing frozen, even three-course dinners: cooked with and served with wine. *Sacre Bleu!* As large as life Julia Child arrived with her culinary foreign words like *sauteuse* in which she 'clarified' pounds of butter, brandishing long sharp knives from Paris, flipping *omelettes*, strewing fresh herbs, pouring liberally from bottles of vermouth as she "deglazed", madly "flambéing" Grand Marnier over *crepes Suzettes*, pulling and popping corks on wines from Burgundy and Bordeaux and Champagne to serve with dinner. (Yes, "*Flûte!*" too bad she and *Grace* never met!)

Radcliffe students are bright and are over-achievers. Most early learn how to manage time, else they would not have much social life. So when I announced before dinner one Wednesday evening to the sherry-imbibing, Mozart-listening throng that Julia Child's *École des Trois Gourmands'* "French Chef" was on local PBS on Monday evenings, I was not surprised to find only three of the residents joining me in the tiny room reserved for the one miniscule black and white television the next Monday. This was 1964 and while Briggs Hall residents enjoyed maintaining tradition, practicing gastronomy was far from most Radcliffe inquiring minds.

That night proved to be a delight. First we saw Pablo Casals's master class in cello from Puerto Rico. Then I remember some political piece with guest William Buckley fired our minds. Primed, we were mesmerized by Julia making *cuisine* magic in her amazing tones and moves until finally traditionally serving while she poured a glass—or two—of accompanying wine, with her glorious and foreign *"Bon Appétit!"*

While by 1964 many households had blithely foregone these dining rituals and were firm advocates of Frozen, our slowly-growing Monday night group were committed to Julia's way. After a month of weeks we sort of mutually decided why not try to replicate one of Julia's dishes? And if it was half as good as she said we would serve it to ourselves. And perhaps to fellow residents?

"Bon." Julia nodded her approval and served us more sherry. *"Continuez; boutez,"* she gestured me onward.

So began an odyssey into cooking with Julia in my Briggs Hall apartment kitchen. While Grace and her large kitchen provided what they could of the ingredients and implements, on Tuesdays I, accompanied by one of our gourmands, would shop for the rest of the list. And Tuesday afternoon or night, we would divide up the work and make like Julia Child. It must have been crazy fun because we kept at it throughout that year.

Then, out of the blue, Julia made one thing we decided to replicate that caused misery throughout Briggs Hall.

Coquille gratinéed in their shells.

Julia devoted two sequential Monday nights to Atlantic seafood and crustacean dishes. On the first night she served *gratinéed* crustaceans in seashells. The following week she gave a class on how to cure those shells which one would use for serving the finished product.

The *École de* Briggs Hall *Gourmettes* decided this would be our next attempt at *Bon Appétit* Julia style.

Soon as we gathered to make a list of the ingredients, we knew we had a problem; one which even Grace could not solve. From where would we get those shells?

As from the god Mercury, the answer was delivered in the form of a Spring Break Invitation. One of our Gourmettes was invited to spend Spring Break in Palm Beach, Florida. Florida!—*Grace au dieu de la cuisine*, this invitation became an opening wide window of opportunity we needed. Our *Gourmette* invitee would find those sea shells for us to cure so we could replicate Julia's *gratinée*.

Check shells off the list.

A week later, Ann 'Spinner' Richards returned with a suitcase full of deep coquille shells. They were beautiful. And did they need that curing! Their stink was ghastly; the muscles were still in the shells. How she got that suitcase into the plane and was allowed to bring so increasingly a smelly thing all the way to Briggs Hall must remain a mystery, until Ann decides to tell.

Of course we were not daunted. After all, our goddess Julia had not seemed in the least overcome by the task. So we borrowed a large soup pot from Briggs Hall kitchens and, holding our noses, did as Julia showed us: First Julia advised oiling and then baking the shells to get the last remnants of the former occupants out, in effect 'curing' the shells. Oh, that was gaggingly hard to take. After fifteen minutes we had to flee the premises. Thank goodness, while running, with napkins over our noses, I remembered to grab the baby. Constance thought this a grand adventure with her favorite baby-sitters included. Grace came marching from the kitchen, a napkin over her face too, not looking as a muse should. The 'Bells Desk' attendee, rushing out, evacuating her sacred post to the smell, left the front door open, where it stayed for several hours. The smell was sickening. We all hovered in the cross-campus. And any residents inside at this unfortunate moment streamed out not looking happy. But, the Spring day was a glorious one. Finally, as more and more joined us, the matter became hilarious. Deciding to make the best of it, someone got a hockey puck and some sticks and everyone ran about. And all windows stayed opened so fresh breezes could, while not as fast as I would have wanted, clear the horror out.

But! *Flûte*! It was not over. Julia had told us to next boil those shells so to completely evacuate any remaining particles. The first step evacuated the premises. While this second step did not yield so dramatic a result, for a few more hours, the stink continued, though less overwhelmingly. All windows stayed open until night. The baby did not seem to notice. In 1965 aromatic sprays for rooms did not yet exist.

Pouring Julia the last of the Lapsang Souchong on that Spring day of 1990, I finished this story of our success in making *coquilles St. Jacques gratinée a la Provençale.*

Julia finished her cup, and, with emphasis confided, *"Flûte, Madeleine!* Coquilles left dead in a shell for more than three hours was not part of my equation."* She recalled open doors in the studio while she finished the same process. "But mine were fresh. What a ghastly surprise for you." She crunched an almond energetically. "Wish I had been there. I could have coined 'Smellavision'," she warbled.

The precepts as Briggs Hall evinced were allied with those upon which Julia's sense of self was founded, those which Julia practiced. She was forward-thinking and modern but abided by traditions of family and history. And her fervor for sticking with and building upon history definitely took root and flourished as she learned and practiced and taught the principals of classical cuisine. So all such tales about how her precepts affected the next generation really interested Julia, just as she was interested in everything adventurous and creative, especially if it involved a good meal too. She said how much she would have enjoyed being in on our culinary sessions. Wouldn't we have loved that, to see our dream, our new world *Marianne Marseillaise,* step out of that little TV and into my tiny kitchen, brandishing her *fouet* and knives! She would have knocked us down with her *Bon appétit!* In 1964 and 1965 we were already like rambunctious ducks following in her train.

The residents of Briggs Hall culinary circle were not the only ones to be out there essaying Julia's gourmandizing. By 1965 much of America's sudden Julia-inspired culinary demands caused a blossoming of kitchen equipment stores, all trying to imitate Julia's favorite store, Paris's legendary

E. Dehillerin, each providing what Julia called a *Batterie de Cuisine*, stocking copper bowls for whipping with the necessary *fouet ballon*, knives of all dimensions and blades—each suitable for its own particular operation, *pince* of many sizes, molds and racks, pots and pans.

America was taking the kitchen back into its heart. All thanks to the extroverted goddess of butter, who made us laugh at her slips and rejoice at her dinner table, toasting with her, "Julia Child, *Bon appétit!*" who taught us that even mistakes are delicious. *BOUTER!*

Chapter 3
Julia Loved Guys

Julia loved men.

Photo courtesy of Cal Poly Pomona, The Collins College of Hospitality Management

In this photo taken December 1, 2000, at The Collins College of Hospitality Management at Cal Poly in Pomona, California, on Julia's honorary doctorate presentation, the Chefs surrounding her are: Michel Richard, Roberto Gerometta, Felician Cueff, Patrick Jeffroy, Alain Gireau, Christopher Gros, Mark Tarbell, Mary Jane Espiritu, and Ernest Briones. This photo shows Julia at her happiest: surrounded by adoring men. For this special occasion I offered Champagne Gosset's delicious Rosé.

Julia's naturally ebullient and happy personality made her a party-girl. She liked to have fun. She particularly loved being with men, especially if they, with adoring looks, were dressed in starched white coats, surrounding her, their goddess of cuisine. I saw this image of her so surrounded by a masculine (and growing feminine. too) sea of white many times, only the faces changed: Her smile is ever broad and her eyes shining.

This was especially so each June in Aspen at the "Food and Wine Classic" when, on opening night, she was greeted by all the new "Young Chefs". The Young Chefs were of course a group she was particularly pleased to meet because she could touch, perhaps even squeeze, the results of her years of instilling and fostering of classical gastronomy. Through them she could actually see and taste the principals of fine cuisine being passed to and practiced with joy and individuality by the next generations. While she was always an interested promoter for every woman chef I ever saw her encounter, in those 1990 years in Aspen her adoring fans were 90% cute guys, and, with that, Julia had no problem.

Julia's natural love of men blossomed when she met her future husband, Paul.

This is a 'Julia Story' *she* liked, and one she felt compelled to tell one afternoon…

"Paul made me realize I was alive," her voice warbled a mite wobblily that afternoon in 1991.

She and I had had lunch together at Chef Michel Richard's Citronelle in Santa Barbara, where we feasted on just harvested, sautéed in butter, golden chanterelles. Now we were back at her Seaview condominium overlooking the Pacific. It was almost 4 PM, and her uncharacteristically hesitating warble was syncopated by a slightly unsteady walk toward where I was sitting as she emerged from her daily, hour-long phone call to her husband. Religiously she checked her watch and, wherever she was she timed her calls to reach Paul at six PM EST just before his dinner. Today her hesitation and disorientation were due to her continuing adjustment to the huge emotional change she daily dealt with since 1989. In 1989 she'd had to part from her '*âme*', her soul; Paul needed constant professional care: That was some mountain to scale and conquer, even for our *Marseillaise de la cuisine*.

She stared out at the Pacific. "When I joined the OSS in 1943, as much as I loved being patriotic I was fleeing a boring Pasadena, a safe life. Not that I didn't, don't, and still do like to play golf; but a diet of golf and card-playing would have killed me a lot quicker than butter ever will, *chérie*," she chortled and plopped into a chair.

I poured her a glass of *Chateauneuf du Pape blanc* from Château la Nerthe, which bottle we could not finish at lunch.

She opened her closed eyes. We clinked. "*Carillon*" in unison we tolled, and, taking a swallow and a breath, Julia continued, looking more inward than out at the sudden rain bouncing on the Ocean below. "I was far from knowing what it was I hoped for in life, but I knew it had to be elsewhere. So I found a good cause, for which I was shipped around the world. In 1943, with nine other girls in our **Oh-So-Secret** group, I adventured out from the good ole USA,—not far from here,—out there, from Los Angeles harbor," she gestured south, "on a navy transport with three thousand men I sailed away. One of our girls, brought up by Missionary parents in Peking, taught Chinese, up on the top deck, for the month plus we were in transit. Joining our group was the husband of anthropologist Margaret Mead, from whom I learned the importance of asking questions. After a month of close living over often bumpy seas we landed in Bombay. And during a long week on land we girls shared somewhat larger living quarters with four-inch cockroaches and swam with delighted-at-seeing-us baby elephants displaying three foot cock fireworks." She stretched her long arm and guffawed. "Such an adventure! But that one pales in memory to those I have of *after* the dusty, humid train ride across India." While they were almost overcome by clouds of dust and incomparable heat, these did not diminish Julia's relish for learning about everything: Buddhism-colors-tastes-aromas-people-voices-designs all bathed over her in that dust and steamy humidity. "Maybe, I thought, the wind in my hair, I would find myself on the Road to Mandalay? And one day I did. Well, Kandy, Sri Lanka, is not Mandalay, but it *is* across the Bay.

"In 1944 I got based to a tea plantation in Ceylon's capitol of Kandy. And there I met the most interesting man I will ever meet; the man who would do more for me than the OSS; the man who would change my world forever. The Kingdom of Kandy was the apotheosis of the land in which I should have fallen in love with Paul." She waxed lyrical, telling of "a land as far from Pasadena as can be imagined was Ceylon." She described a green place of leopards and elephants, of ibises and exotic flowers, "…a land of monsoons," she waved at outside at the increasing drenching going on below, and told about a land in which the mystical and sacred touch the profane, a land of bells and temples, of gigantic and tranquil representations of Buddha.

Paul gravitated to learning about all of the wonders of Ceylon. He put out his feelers of intellect and passion on this magical carpet ride, taking Julia along for the grand unveiling to "restaurants of flavors and colors I'd not tasted before, to temples and on elephant rides. How could I resist falling madly, uncontrollably in love with this interesting and interested man, part poet and painter, cartographer and photographer, lover and *bon viveur*? Uncontrollably, I tell you. Only, with all his interests, he wasn't interested in me."

Paul, an older, self-taught intellectual, enjoyed a reputation for numerous amorous conquests. His first meetings with Julia did not leave him with those displays of joy the young elephants had regaled her group with. He felt he was experienced too far beyond what Julia needed. But then, that apotheotic land of Kandy worked its magic on Paul too. After many gazings into those intelligent eyes and many seeings of Julia's longings and desires, feeling her hot commitment to his, Paul's knees became putty, and he too found himself also increasing in another passion.

"A passion called 'falling in love', with leggy me." She stretched out her long legs and saw them as they were in 1944, through thirty-two year old eyes of a loved one.

Never, once this woman's gaze fastened on his with interest in all things artistic and aesthetic, a woman who could not get enough of what Paul gave her inquiring mind, nor obviously enough of what he gave Julia's passionate nature, did he, could he, look beyond those long gorgeous gams. A man who intricately carved furniture, painted and knew about food and wine, found himself thrilled at his desire to share these talents and knowledge with this "gaga-over-him" dame who took to it all like a duck. "Quack, quack," she trilled.

It was through this variously talented man that Julia first felt herself awakening to herself and awakening to the possibilities within herself. Paul was the magician whose kiss encouraged the Pasadena Princess to life. And did she love him for it!! How could he not return such passion? There was never again another gal for Paul.

"Ever after, Paul introduced me to life in all its wonders. That was his greatest gift." The rain pounded, and Julia's voice grew quiet. Her memories of that young, vibrant man sorely contrasted with the Paul she'd just conversed with, a Paul who could not finish sentences or remember what he'd had for lunch. By 1989 his abilities had so diminished that he needed constant care. But, no matter the quality of care, there was no reversing the situation.

"*Défense d'afficher!*" I slapped the table to break the spell.

"*Défense de Cracher!*" The spell broken, Julia laughingly returned to now. Her eyes reflected the Ocean.

These 'Defense' phrases must be important to the French psyche because they are enduring. To the two of us they were hysterically funny French 'forbiddens'. Both are splashed across walls throughout France, from Paris to every hamlet and village. "It is Forbidden to Post Signs!"

"NO Spitting!" There are others just as funny making them interchangeable by us in getting laughs like *"Défense de Pisser"* and *"Défense de Fumer"*.

I'll say it again, Julia was a party girl. I cannot remember an invitation offered that she refused if she was on the same side of the USA as the proposed event. Like that 1991 lunch we shared at Citronelle.

Not long after, one afternoon I ran to pick up the phone and heard my name pronounced the French way but warbled as only one person could. *"Madeleine,"* her voice rose, giving away that she had some good news. Of course I could not know that this call from my tall friend would signal the embarkation of an odyssey with Julia that would last until 1996. *"Madeleine,"* she trilled.

"Julia," I replied, also pronouncing *her* name *a la française*, the accent falling on the 'a'. *"Comment vas-tu, Julia?"*

"Très, très bien, chérie. I'm calling to invite myself to visit you. It's been much too long since I've been there."

"I agree." By her anticipatory excitement I knew she already had some delight in mind, "would you like me to arrange a golf game for you, Julia?" (She loved to play golf.)

"Non, non, chère amie. I don't want to play golf. At least not this time."—Since 1980 Julia's knees had been giving her pain. She had had surgery. At this moment was not in much pain; but why tempt fate? —

"Well, the season is perfect for swimming. So come for as long as you like and we'll swim and while you're here I'll bring you to check out golf courses for the next time. In fact why don't we plan a Julia Child Golf Tournament to raise funds for the AIWF? You can ride from hole to hole dispensing tees and Champagne," I began planning. "And at night we'll have dinners at restaurants where the *chefs* will adore to …"

Julia interrupted …"*that's it!* **Chefs!** That's what I want to do. I want to meet all the chefs in Palm Springs. I don't have long to be there. Only one day; in fact, only that afternoon. You see, before I meet all the chefs at your house, you are coming with me to have lunch where someone is giving me an award. Then, *flûte,* I have to get to San Francisco for a Planned Parenthood fund-raiser. So just that afternoon will be for us to visit and for me to meet all the chefs; all the chefs in the desert, *chez Madeleine.*"

Before I finished saying how much fun that would be, she was telling me to tell all those chefs to bring any cook books they would like her to sign, "even if they are not mine!" she chortled. Julia was always stoked to meet chefs and talk food and recipes. And she loved signing her name.

But when I checked my calendar I was dismayed to say I could not accompany her to the lunch because I had several wine appointments that whole morning. So it was set: I would not go to the lunch. And Julia would arrive here around 2:30 PM. to meet all the chefs of Palm Springs.

Besides my getting to welcome Julia at my home again, for me the other very good news was the hour: 2:30 PM. Julia and the chefs would have had a good lunch. *Madeleine* did not have to prepare food for such critical palates.

The morning of the event I put three cases of Champagne bottles deep into ice, and polished some fifty Champagne tulips before taking off for my appointments. When I drove up to my house at 2 PM there was already a white jacketed bouquet of approximately ten chefs, some sporting tall toques, standing outside my front door chatting away excitedly: the first party I'd ever given where the guests came half an hour early. By the time I lassoed this group inside, putting frosty glasses of Champagne into their wildly gesturing and chopping hands, through the front door was coming a steady stream of more and more starched white jackets. Cook books, most looking like dinner had often been served on them, were piling up near the fireplace in anticipation.

It took moving the Champagne cart and a little pushing to get these guys outside by the pool on such a beautiful day and not crushed, stuck together in the kitchen. Not until the next day did it dawn on me that perhaps they thought Julia was going to do a demonstration?

"*Flûte!*"

Champagne's bubbles elevate the alcohol to the brain twice as fast as that of still wines, and therefore, spirits raised, laughter is the sure-to-follow result. By 2:30 the Champagne corks were popping, and Champagne's laughter was almost deafening throughout my house. As I passed through, filling glasses, the talk was all of food, described with gestures of preparation and lots of 'tack, tack, tack" accompanied by cutting motions. "*Non, non*"; "*oui oui ...*"

Thirty to forty chefs all talking at once is very loud. When the guest of honor stepped through the front door and stooped to give me a hug, I had to ask her to repeat what she'd said: I could not hear a word.

So in her most trilling tones Julia spoke words that filled me with dread, "What's there to eat?"

My eyes popped wide; my heart skipped a beat. "Eat?" What happened to our plan? What to say to the goddess of our tummies? "Oh dear me, Julia," I tried whispering back, "there's, there's—nothing."

Now her eyes got wide. "Nothing? Nonsense!" she trilled.

"Didn't you just have a fine lunch? Actually, *chère amie,"* I swallowed, "there really is nothing."

Julia stood tall and announced, "the lunch was so dreadful even the rolls were inedible." She looked at me with hunger in her eyes and righteousness in her Chef Max Bugnard-trained heart.

Fast I grabbed her down to my height and whispered, "Shussh. That chef, directly in back of me, is the one who prepared your lunch."

For a moment her gaze fell full on his unhearing back, then she swept herself and me away through the house to the kitchen. "Nothing, *Madeleine?* Nonsense. We will find something." Julia was dreaming an impromptu demonstration of how to make cuisine with left-overs. She opened the refrigerator with an anticipatory air. She stooped; she searched; she stood up and faced me, "Nothing." Then she grabbed the handle to the freezer and with a smile like the cat about to get cream, she opened. And looked. "Nothing," she confirmed.

"Yes, something," I stammered, "but you cannot eat batteries and coffee beans. I've been travelling and have not gotten to the market. Oh Julie I am so sorry."

"Flûte!"

She could see I was about to cry, so she patted me on the head. "Don't worry, I'll find something." We both took good swallows of frothy cold Champagne, and forthwith began going through all the cupboards in the pantry. One, two, three; click, click, click; we closed one after the other. Four, five. Finally: "Told you!" she pounced and stood, brandishing a tall bottle of Greek Kalamata olives.

Quickly I produced a bowl and decanted olives for her, our Athena.

"Et, voici, et voilà!" Triumphant, Julia waved a large sack of Maui Kettle-style potato chips. "A feast, *petite!"* She chomped down on olives.

E. Delacroix: Le 28 Juillet; la Liberté guidant le peuple, 1830 (RF 129)
Paris, musée du Louvre, acquis au Salon de 1831

Another bowl was found by her embarrassed un-hostess, *moi,* and armed with two bowls full of not-very-filling treats, Julia and I set forth to meet the adoring, getting-tipsy throng. And, though weak with near starvation, she went graciously from one chef to the next, listening to each and every story about how her TV programs changed their lives; how, though a mother forbad television until all homework was done, Julia's shows were clandestinely watched, and in the long run proud parents were the result. While she moved through the rooms these stories and family recipes seemed to return her to life, but never were those two bowls far from her side. She or I would move them from one spot to the next close enough for a quick handful. When one starched white sleeve or another attempted a chip or an olive I was quick to shake a finger, "No. Julia is hungry."

The proof of this fantastic and dreadfully embarrassing story is found in the photo above. You see Julia, with a handful of potato chips, her smile betraying her dilemma of how, in her effort to stave off eminent demise, to consume as many of those crispy chips as quickly as possible while maintaining composure. Talking with her is Adam Zack, owner and wine-guru of Palm Springs's Gourmet markets. On the sideboard, well within arm's reach in back, are the bowls, one of the chips, one of the olives, *and* it looks like *another* one with tomatoes! Julia must have conjured them.

Not a very gracious way to welcome the woman who saved us all from death by frozen dinners.

Unfortunately every chef in town was at my house; not one restaurant was open to call for a quick saving delivery. How could I live with myself after starving Julia Child at my home? What could I do to make amends? "Julia,"—I swear as I hugged her at the airport some hours later I heard her stomach rumble. "Oh, Julia, I am dreadfully sorry. And I promise to make it up to you with a huge and delicious meal the very next time we get together."

She stumbled a little as she took the steps to the plane, the result of too much Champagne and nothing to eat. I was sure I heard her back saying, "Nevermore!"

Julia was opposite from most mortals, in case you haven't noticed. Her schedule was one that would have leveled most people decades younger. Now while I have said that Julia was a party girl, loving to attend gatherings and movies, actually most of her life after *Cordon Bleu* was decidedly one of hard work, all of which fed her gustatory enthusiasms and talent for organization. Daily she was scripting new shows, while working on another cookbook following the shooting of each of her TV series on Cooking in all its aspects and varieties. Year-after-year many of her letters and cards say practically the same thing: "Am finishing the new television …;" "am on the PR tour for …" all interchangeable except for the dates. In mid-August she'd pack goodies, including the annual Birthday cake I sent from one or another of America's Master Bakers, and congregate with her Child family in Maine for a big birthday. After the 1994 clan gathering (which was also a family tribute for Paul and private scattering of his ashes), back in Cambridge she wrote about all the work there was yet to do that year …

JULIA CHILD'S KITCHEN
103 Irving Street
Cambridge, MA 02138
Tel: (617) 876 1072
Fax: (617) 491 2347

August 18, 1994

Madeleine de Jean
P.O. Box 2491
Palm Springs, CA 92263

Dear Madeline:

Thanks so much for your jolly birthday greetings. You were kind to remember.

We just completed taping 26 new shows for our "Cooking With Master Chefs" series, but I shall continue to work on the companion cookbook for weeks to come! There is a great deal to be done between now and next spring when the program airs! Here's hoping you are enjoying the summer, and are gearing up for a busy fall!

With all good wishes,

Julia

This love Song of Work rarely changed. In November of 1999 from Cambridge she wrote, "our new television series will commence the end of the month and the book is finally out! I think it is a beauty! Anyway I will be traveling about on a PR tour several weeks ..." After mid-June's Aspen Classic appearances, in July and in August before and after her family

Birthday celebration in Maine, she'd host and shoot the next television series in her Cambridge Mass home. From 1992 to 2000 her score read, "we are gearing up for the PR tour for our new PBS television series and companion cookbook. It promises to be our (never 'my') best book yet."

In December or November she'd return to Santa Barbara for the winter months (especially after closing their *La Peetch* [Julia for *La Pitchoune*] house in Provence in 1992). "I'm here in Santa Barbara working hard on the new book. So I'm staying put except for tours. Come visit." Or, "I will be traveling for another PR tour and fund raising for Planned Parenthood. When will we get together? Save December. Santa Barbara." This was the Sublime Extrovert's plea for company. While she was completely independent Julia really loved having people to chat with or to bounce ideas off. Julia was gregarious. Could you guess?

In 1991 when Julia was 79, though she'd already had knee replacement surgery more than once, she was showing every sign of increasing her work schedule if possible. Except for the odd moment when she faced starvation. (*Mea culpa.*) So while we spoke often in the weeks following my grave *faux pas*, most of the time Julia was either back in Cambridge hard at work, or travelling all over the US and Italy and France doing demonstrations with chefs or privately teaching. Though this meant extra strain on her damaged knees, Julia loved teaching one-on-one as much as performance teaching. Between her schedule and mine, actually inking-in a date for me to try to make-up for my criminal treatment of Julia's well-being was daily going futuristic, month by ticking month.

"I have it," she shouted one day regarding my broken-record plea to compensate for my dastardly neglect of our goddess. "Aspen! The *Food and Wine* Classic! Mid June!" I heard her smack her desk. "*Bouter en avant.*" With that "*Bouter*" I knew "Nevermore" was fading to "Forgiven". (Julia took every opportunity to act on her motto, mimicking 'Full Steam Ahead!')

"Perfect." I could hardly believe we'd at least found a time and place where I could regain my self-respect and salvation from the tantalizing hell to which all who starve Julia get sent. "I'll be there with John Scharffenberger. I promise a wonderful meal and delicious wines, ending your recurring nightmares of starvation at my hands." I could hear her chortle over the line. (Or maybe she was choking.) "How about the Wednesday before the whole thing gets underway?" I proposed.

"Great," she coughed. "Wednesday, it is!" She rustled the pages of her diary. "Oh, yikes; no can. That's the moment the Young Chefs meet with me. No, not Wednesday." That meeting to introduce Julia to the year's Young Chefs was sacred.

So we flipped through the calendar for the rest of the week in Aspen. Thursday, Friday, Saturday all went past. It was not until we got to the last day, just when I was fearing my salvation might again be put in the freezer with the batteries and coffee beans, that Julia found it: "Sunday lunch after all the programs are done. We'll have a gargantuan feast after I've carried the last pot and blowtorch through town and can totally relax." (One of Julia's cooking stunts that had her fans on the edge of their seats was her demonstration of how to caramelize to glassy perfection the sugar crust on *crème brûlée*. While Jacques Pepin would take out a small chef's torch, Julia would arrive with a humongous one capable of blowtorching Jacques's *crème brûlée* to a cinder. Or perhaps she would arrive with a huge fire extinguisher, wearing an oversized fireman's hat? The audience could not get enough of her extravagances, or whatever details of an intricate dish she might wow them with. But "please, *please*," everyone prayed to the gods of food, "let her mention the 'Food Police'!")

Chapter 4
Save Julia Child From Starvation
Picnics in Aspen

Tasting FOOD and WINE Under the TENTS at Aspen

Before it became 'Aspen Colorado's *Food and Wine* Classic' this gastronomic event was started in 1984 by Gary Plumley, owner of Aspen's iconic wine shop, "Of Grapes and Grain." In 1984 he, and two partners, devised an event utilizing the skills and culinary uniqueness of each of Aspen's chefs, coupling those with various wines to accompany, all designed to give life to an in-between, "dead", but gorgeous, season in Aspen.

After a few years of growing audience appreciation, the festival became too big to handle locally. For a week prior, the parking lot behind

"Of Grapes and Grain" wine shop was fenced off and patrolled by armed guards night and day because the stacked cases of wines arriving by the truck-load had no other place to rest except there. The logistics, once able to be handled by off-season, un-busy hotel and restaurant staff members, quickly grew beyond the town's capacity. Just getting enough ice and delivery trucks to the wine tents had become a nightmare. By 1990 a perfect sponsor was found in *Food and Wine* Magazine, and the new Aspen 'Food and Wine' Classic was born. By 1992 this was THE Internationally recognized and attended foodie event with Chefs and Wine-makers introducing dishes and vintages of pride, with attending coveted prizes for the creators.

And this became the food and wine festival at which Julia gave her signature performances and presence; and now the festival where my return to grace would happen.

During the Aspen 'Food and Wine' Classic Julia always stayed at Aspen's Silver Lode era, 1880s beauty, Hotel Jerome, right in the center of town on the corner of Main and Mill streets. Loving history and delighting in knowing the current management practiced The Jerome standard of modern excellence with a Victorian feel, Julia gravitated to staying there.

The Hotel Jerome was often my home-away-from-home hotel, as was its General Manager my favorite General Manager. "Hello, Tony." The day Julia and I settled that my salvation would happen on the Sunday at the end of the Classic, I placed this call to arrange all with Tony DiLucia.

Photo of Tony DiLucia outside of the Hotel Jerome by Belinda Oster

"Madeleine, when are you coming to town?"

Tony is always up for a bubbly escapade, and over the years I worked with him we had become friends. We both love to combine business with adventures. We both love great Champagne. And Tony is a Cornell CIA graduate. He knows excellence in food and wine assures his guests' return. What more delicious way to succeed?

"Soon. I'll be there next month. But today Tony, I need to plan a lunch, a private lunch, very special, for Julia Child. So, shall we do it?" I gave him the date and time, and he confirmed the space was available. We would hold this lunch poolside so Julia, who will have been inside tents and ballrooms for the previous four days, would get some Alpine sun and breeze before returning east to Cambridge, Mass.

"How many?" Tony continued.

"Well, I have to let you know. I know John Scharffenberger will be with me. We will serve his sparkling wines of course. And I think Julia mentioned she would have her editor or her chief cooking assistant with her. She is going to let me know. Probably, six? At the most."

"Jeff Troiola, our chef, will call you to propose a menu," I could hear 'General' Tony writing down what I had told him.

"Great. We can finalize details when I see you on …" I had a trip planned to Aspen for the following month so we would work it out then.

"Madeleine." It was Julia was on the phone. A week had passed since we confirmed the Aspen date. "Madeleine, I would like to invite Nancy Barr to our lunch. Is that okay?"

"Of course, Julia. And John Scharffenberger, my co-host, and I are thinking we'll invite Harley Baldwin. John's such a sweetheart. You are sure to fall in love. Again."

She laughed. "I think I may already be taken. But that's all wonderful. The more the merrier, yes? Oh. Maybe I *will* invite…"

And so we talked. After we hung up I called to let the Hotel Jerome know that the guest list was raised to nine.

Three weeks later when the list had expanded to fifteen, on a snowy Spring morning in Aspen I met up with Chef Jeff in his kitchen.

"I'm thinking a four-course, French meal," Jeff whisked butter into a velvety sauce. Tony joined us. They led me to the windows overlooking the pool and patio, which were covered in a new blanket of snow. The Chef wiped his hands on a cloth and gestured, "… hors d'oeuvres by the pool, and the first plate of perhaps …" I listened to a well-structured French meal, served formally, and was thinking of that patio divested of snow, with the mid-June sun baking us outside by the pool; thinking of the week Julia—and all the rest of us attending the Food and Wine Classic—would have enjoyed of tastings and complex meals of rich dishes. When Chef Jeff got to the Baked Alaska for desert I spoke up.

"Marvelous; my goodness, that's an Escoffier-inspired sequence. Appetizing. Tantalizing. But. May I …?." I suggested what I had envisioned of a meal that would deliciously assuage any hunger pangs Julia ever felt because of me. But this lunch should also be fun for all to enjoy being together, outdoors, table-hopping, sabering, sparkling bubbles encouraging singing perhaps, laughing certainly: A summer luncheon.

Tony said, "As of now Madeleine cannot say how many will attend. So, for a growing group, let's rethink? Sunday lunch, after four days and nights of large meals and tastings of heavy and elaborate dishes."

The chef's brow furrowed; he was deep in thought, picturing anew.

We all were. Suddenly, like a light bulb being switched on it came clear. "How about creating an old-fashioned American picnic?" I spoke our thought. "The French invented it: *un déjeuner sur l'herbe*. I bet in Escoffier you can find something quite perfect and divine."

Tony was there. "But, how about an American Fourth of July picnic? Yes! Let's invite Julia and our guests to an old fashioned Fourth-of-July-style picnic, poolside at the Jerome?"

Jeff was feeling it.

Tony walked us through it. "A month from now the Jerome will be somewhat less-than-busy—our off-season. But, Jeff, remember how desperately busy you, and your whole staff, will be those five days *before* this Sunday lunch. You all will be at the breaking point with the number of events and meals for the crowds here during the Food and Wine Classic."

We both heard Chef Jeff sigh. "No great French lunch to impress Julia," must have been his thoughts. That's a dream hard for any Chef to let go of. Aloud, with renewed gusto, he said, "Fried chicken? Potato salad? And chocolate cake?"

"That's it! That's the menu. The 'Save Julia Child From Starvation Picnic' menu at The Hotel Jerome." Tony and I spoke in unison, hugging the chef.

So it was set. We had a menu. I hoped. I had to pass it by the guest of honor.

"Fabulous," Julia trilled into the phone. "I love fried chicken. And never get it. *Coq au vin*; yes, of course with a great Burgundy sauce and another bottle to drink. *Poulet Chasseur* too I adore. Roast chicken; yum. Those I am served all the time. Fried chicken it is, *chère ami*. We'll be just like a family. Oh, did I ask you? May I bring…?

And so it went. The menu was approved. Though the number of guests the Chef would be coking for was not yet as clear. But Chef Jeff would offer Julia a delightful and restorative meal, assuring my salvation.

In mid-June, under a brilliant blue sky, I, with my co-host John Scharffenberger, and Tony DiLucia, offered Julia Child an appeasement meal poolside at The Hotel Jerome. I sent out, to the growing guest list, invitations on post cards I purchased from the Metropolitan Museum showing Edouard Manet's 1863 racy painting called "*Déjeuner sur l'herbe*" just to give a hint of *French* decadences a picnic might lead to: more than fending off starvation was a possibility:

Luncheon on the Grass - by Édouard Manet reprinted with permission by *Musée d'Orsay*, Paris

The day and the hour arrived. While thirty-five guests, surfeited after a week of being stuffed gastronomically and over indulged by wines, arrived and accepted frosty glasses of Scharffenberger sparkling Brut from Mendocino vineyards, Julia Child, John Scharffenberger, and Tony DiLucia, almost by automatic thought, stood, one next to the other, front and center, each with a cold bottle and an implement. In a wave they sabered one after the other, shooting corks over the front gate into Main Street, and the first Julia Child Picnic at The Hotel Jerome was in session. (Julia 'sabered' with a tea spoon, while John and Tony used chef's knives.)

With that opening salvo, the first course was presented. Chef Jeff's potato salad was indeed a potato salad. But one which your American grandmother might not recognize.

The author with Chef Jeff

It was filled with grilled shrimp and seared fresh tuna, speckled with capers and *Niçoise* olives, with tiny pink tomatoes and of course darling baby new potatoes, all dressed with an olive-oil rich *Provençal* dressing, resting on multi-colored lettuces. Yes, that was a great first course for a picnic to assuage hunger pangs. And Chef Jeff got his first *French* picnic dish in!

Julia and her nephew-in-law
Photo by M. Hill and K. Packer

Julia was digging in and slugging down the bubbly, and I knew I could live.

Photo by M. Hill and K. Packer

She smiled, raised her glass, and across the space we mouthed, "*carillon*" and drank Scharffenberger brut. Hurray!

Photo by Steve Mundinger, Aspen Studios

The crisp, fried chicken we washed down with Scharffenberger's *Rosé brut*, and heaven was near. Everyone was talking over each other. Obviously this Save Julia Child Picnic had legs. No one would go home hungry today.

Then *it* arrived.

(Do you think with this '*it*' I am going to bust this bubble with a dreadful tale? Read on.)

Then *it*, The Chocolate Cake to cry tears of joy for, arrived.

Photo by author

About six inches tall and dripping (in the sun) chocolate. The recipe could only have come from Henri-Paul Pellaprat's tome: "a genoise cake with chocolate butter cream, and chocolate fondant icing." Jeff got in another French dish, one with six layers! Bravo, Chef!

Pinch-hitting in the sommelier role, I was able to greet each guest upon arrival, serving the first frosty glass of Scharffenberger bubbles. And, near the end of lunch, I became the cake server, getting a chance to see our guests at the point of most contentment and hear some of their latest adventures. Naturally the guest of honor, *Madame la Raison d'Etre,* got the first chocolate chocolate slice, and another glass of *Rosé.* Julia gave my cheek a chocolate kiss and whispered, "Do let's do it again next year?"

Photo by Steve Mundinger, Aspen Studios

We toasted on that.

A chocolate *bisou* and toast with Scharffenberger *Rosé* ended the first annual Save Julia Child Picnic at the Hotel Jerome. And so commenced a luncheon-gathering to stave off starvation for Julia that would grow with each of us. "Forgiven. I'm forgiven!" I did a little dance.

While Julia was anticipating returning to Cambridge for a busy summer season working on new companion cookbooks for her most recent television series, first she had a more pressing duty, one less anticipated. With her niece, Phila, Julia went to *Provence* for a last visit, to pack up her *batterie de cuisine,* and shutter her home there for the last time.

Paul Child photo: permission by Schlesinger Library

Julia had faced that Paul would no longer be accompanying her to *La Pitchoune*, the Roman-tiled-roof home surrounded by olive trees and lavender, bathed in magical Provençal light they had together built on the property of her close friend and collaborator, Simca. By gentlemanly agreement *La Peetch* would be offered to the Fischbacher/Thibault families when Julia and Paul were no longer able to use it. During the past few years Julia's closest friends, collaborators, and frequent visitors, Jim Beard and Simca herself, had died. And now with Paul's inability to join her there, Julia knew this was the moment. She packed and handed over the key as they'd promised all those years ago. That done, Julia faced west, ready to *Bouter en avant.* "Next," was her goal, *comme toujours.*

Back in Cambridge Julia returned to the schedule she was most comfortable with, working on yet another cookbook before taking off on a whirlwind Fall PR tour for the most recent PBS series they had finished shooting. After her annual August birthday celebration in the Child's stronghold in Maine, despite recurring knee pain, she jumped into writing and PR touring and fund-raising before and after another knee-straining cooking class at Venice's Cipriani Hotel in October.

By November I began getting her signals in the form of cards and letters telling me when she would be returning to Santa Barbara. Julia liked visitors, and I would be one. But before that I must not get ahead of myself.

The overwhelming success of the family-style picnic that saved me from perpetual embarrassment, and Julia from starvation, dictated it would continue.

Fact: After hard work, Julia liked to have fun.

While by 1990 Julia had endured more than four knee surgeries, in June 1993 back and forth across Aspen Julia was walking strong and well, carrying her weight, it seemed, in cast iron skillets and gadgets, all over town to her various demonstrations. By the end of the week she was up for fun and fried chicken.

Le déjeuner sur l'herbe by Claude Monet reprinted with permission by *Musée d'Orsay*, Paris

"You are cordially invited to once more save Julia from Starvation at the Hotel Jerome."

For the 1993 'Saving Julia' some 75 guests accepted my invitation, sent on cards showing another French Impressionist's *déjeuner*, to our second Save Julia Child Jerome picnic with John Scharffenberger, and I, and Tony, *et* the gal we were going to once again save, *La JULIA*. Local press people were now invited like Pat Miller, Denver-based The Gabby Gourmet, and her husband, Mark. Marcella Hazan, her husband, Victor, son and daughter-in-law were among the first to arrive. Jacques Pepin—I think— came that year. Or maybe it was in 1994? I know Julia's dear long-time friend, and now her special friend, John McJennett, was there. "Meet my 'younger man'," she trilled, eyes shining.

When I sat next to him for some fried chicken, handsome, blond and taller than Julia, and indeed six months younger, John confided that he was, besides Julia's boy-friend, a writer, working on a historical biography about a Wild West character from the 1800s. We got along from the moment we

met, mutually enjoying our conversations. Naturally if Julia loved him he
had lots of brains as well.

Several of my best friends from Aspen were there too, like Harley
Baldwin, creator and owner of the Caribou Club, and Gary Plumley and his
wife Shirley, owners of Aspen's iconic wine shop, Of Grapes and Grain. As
well, Ingrid and Bob Greuter, owners of Aspen Wines enjoyed this
wonderful Sunday afternoon with Julia and Co. The owners of the Grog
Shop joined the festivities that year. Julia's cherished associates, Nancy Barr
and Suzy Davidson naturally were there. Local chefs and restaurateurs like
Walt Harris of 'Syzygy', Jodi from '*Cache-Cache*'; from his eponymous
restaurant, Jimmy was with us; Manager Sommelier, Olivier of the Caribou:
all gabbed with *La Julia*. From Phoenix newly-weds Chef Christopher and
Paola Gros met up with chef friends and serenaded Julia. The Festivities
were ebullient and Julia was front and center, enjoying. Owners of
Scharffenberger's local distributor, Grand Vin, Jane and Jim Krug and Chris
and Mickey Smith with Joe Nazarro were chatting up John Scharffenberger
and Gabby Gourmet.

Again, to start things, we sabered, this time increasing the wave-line
by one: me. And when the corks flew over the front fence there was a
watching crowd over which those missiles had to sail past. The word
was out: Julia was having a picnic and everyone could watch.
(Remember the analogy to the Bourbon Kings performing at supper for
their adoring people?) After the sabering I gave my History-of-The-
Lunch speech, confessing in public to once, two years ago, starving Julia
Child. The crowd groaned. No one threw eggs. And the 1993 picnic was
officially Open to be enjoyed. Nikko had started off the celebration,
toddling next to me as assistant sommelier, helping me serve the
Champagnes. His mother, Phila, Julia's cherished niece, daughter of her
sister, Dort, and Phila's husband Bob, were of course there, adding to
the picnic festivities.

Phila Cousins and son, Nikko, Julia's neice and great nephew.
Photo by M. Hill and K. Packer

When the cake service signaled the time had come to begin our *au revoir*s, Julia's little great-nephew, Nikko, got one of the first pieces.

Julia had forgiven me for sure.

And we were all, as Julia loved to say, "a real little family."

Photograph of our real little family by M. Hill and K. Packer

The 1994 picnic, mid-June, came only a month after Julia's soul-mate, husband of forty-seven years, Paul, died. Paul had been in complete care since 1989. Daily Julia telephoned two or more times when she was gone from Massachusetts, or went there when she was. By 1993, 1994, Paul often wondered who was calling and sometimes did not recognize her own person. This broke Julia's heart.

So I was relieved to receive her note replying to my condolences after his death saying she was looking forward to our "meeting _next week_ in Aspen!" *Bouter en avant!*

Looking forward!

A bit of horror-show gossipy whispers from Julia added additional spice to the pre-opening hour of our 1994 Save Julia Child From Starvation Aspen event: the astonishing Los Angeles police chase of O.J. Simpson's white Bronco captured on camera for national television, lent a sort of "Agatha Christie Orient Express" thriller undercurrent.

Julia describing the White Bronco chase on LA freeway.
Photo by M. Hill and K. Packer

At that 1994 Julia Child Hotel Jerome picnic we hosted some 145 guests. The popularity was spreading like an underground newsletter. That year my invitation was printed on another of Claude Monet's 1865 versions of a French picnic. For the place mats I cut out faces from photos of prior picnics: Julia's, John McJennet's, John Scharffenberger's, Tony DiLucia's, Marcella Hazan's and superimposed them over the faces of Monet's gorgeously attired guests.

Photo by M. Hill and K. Packer

Julia wrote just prior that the picnic was becoming the "hot ticket" in Aspen. Jacques Pepin was there, as well as our regulars like Marcella Hazan and her family. That year a contingency from Palm Springs joined the celebration and we have many photos taken by them of all of us laughing and drinking and eating.

Photo by M. Hill and K. Packer

The Sabering line was again increased by one: Jacques Pepin. Jacques sabered with a butter knife wearing my yellow hat.

Julia maintained her sovereignty of the teaspoon as proper sabering equipment. The ogling crowd at the front gate to watch Julia sending a cork flying overhead, had grown so large there were Aspen police keeping them from falling into the Main Street traffic. The 1994 Julia Child Picnic at The Hotel Jerome was officially Open. And my yellow hat was everywhere.

Photos by M. Hill and K. Packer

When I had a moment to talk with Julia's companion, John McJennett, he was proud to say he was advancing with his Wild West book quite well. While it did not go as fast as he liked he was enjoying the research and the writing.

A writer is always delighted to hear another writer's excitement in uncovering mysteries of the story through some particular gem found in research. John turned his chair to face me so we could hear each other over the laughter and chatter. I asked if he knew the biographies of Yale's American Studies and literature professor R.W.B. Lewis, considered by most as the premier biographer then working in the U.S? John was interested to know more so I promised to send him a copy of Dick Lewis's biography of Edith Wharton.

Julia and John McJennett. Next to him is John Scharffenberger my co-host.

"I *love* R.W.B. Lewis's books." From over my shoulder Julia trilled. "His on Edith Wharton is my favorite. Do you know him, Madeleine?" We pulled over a chair and squeezed together to discussed the importance for a writer of biography, like John, to read other great examples, like Dick's works. I told them about his work on his biography of Florence. "I'm off to Florence in October," she announced. Julia grabbed hold of my offer to send a copy of Dick's *City of Florence* when it was published, "I look forward to reading that, *chère amie.*"

Just as I was about to serve the *pièce de résistance*, the chocolate cake, I grabbed that darling creator of much of the new and happening Aspen, Harley Baldwin, seating him next to Julia and John. For the chocolate cake presentation and service I was once again assisted admirably by Julia's growing great nephew.

Photo by the author of Nikko and his mother Philo.

I cannot imagine the self-control a young child serving chocolate cake to 145 people must have exercised: Never once did I see Nikko lick his chocolate coated fingers. Not until we served his piece.

The guests were mostly gone and, over the last of the chocolate cake Julia and Harley Baldwin and John McJennett and John Scharffenberger and I gathered round, licking our fingers and talking over each other: we were all filled with rosy content that the combo of chocolate and Scharffenberger sparkling *Rosé* can bring. John McJennett was describing his Wild-West character for Harley and John Scharffenberger when ... I remembered ... and interrupted:

"Harley has a painting. One he commissioned from the greatest Native American painter alive. Who lives and works across town," I gestured, "over there: Earl Biss. He painted the Battle of Little Big Horn on the wall in the Caribou Club. It might be oils on wood, but it stories like a reality."

"Any time of day or night, Madeleine can go see it. The Caribou Club's night watchmen, cooks, cleaners, the management staff know she might show up at any time. I do have reports," Harley smiled, "that someone hears a noise, maybe at 4 or 5 AM, and finds her sitting, looking at Earl's painting."

It is true. I am addicted to that painting. "John," I nudged John McJennett, "you must see it. Earl shows the real Wild West that your character lived in. This is an important historic event he depicts. For better understanding of the situation and the problems both nations faced out on the western plains, you must see it. The story we read and hear in school is not told from the side of the Indians."

Julia stood up. "Let's go." she trumpeted.

When Julia stands up she is ready to 'Bouter'. So, full of sparkling Scharffenberger, we strode up the street toward the Caribou Club. Soon in the semi light of an inner room of Harley's club, we were sitting holding hands and gazing up.

Earl Biss painted a frieze around the top of the room. In all its splendor and all its grimness and dust he shows with a blazing talent the battle that took place that one day, from pre-dawn to dusk, the deaths at "The Little Big Horn." While we gazed, there was mostly silence, and Julia's breathing. Holding hands we could stabilize to lean back and turn round and round to take it all in. Finally we sat and, still holding hands, still were silent. Harley left first. Julia stood up. John McJennett was involved interiorly with that day in 1876. This bloody battle, won by no one, he was seeing, maybe really seeing for the first time, hearing the War Cries, smelling, feeling the heat, the anguish of such a battle: He seemed to be breathing in the Wild West he was writing about. But John had served in World War II. Was he also comparing such death and suffering?

Then John stood, and he and Julia reached back for me, and with John Scharffenberger we left the scene of devastation.

Harley was waiting for us at the front door. He pointed to the framed and illustrated letter Earl Biss wrote describing how he painted this work, detailing the pigments used in case any repair was needed and he was not about. Harley read aloud the last sentence—which I paraphrase—"I have another work in another Aspen public building: the Pitkin County Jail."

"'Freedom'," I call it.

"You've seen it?" John McJ. asked.

"Madeleine's called the 'Pitken County Jail docent'," John Scharffenberger laughed.

"Let's *Bouter*!" Julia shouted.

Back across town and across the meadow to Aspen's Pitken County Jail.

While Julia and the two Johns looked at the Silver Lode Era photographs on the walls, I went to ask the receptionists if we could have access to Mr. Biss's painting. She looked at me like at a returning nightmare.

"Now, Madeleine," the Sherriff began as he strode toward me. "I did ask you to make an appointment before dropping by …"—as he spoke he looked into the eyes of my four companions, all of a height and level with his … "Oh, hello Harley," he smiled and shook Harley's hand. "Madeleine," he continued, doing a good job of being patient, "I don't see any…" The Sheriff's eyes widened when his gaze got to Julia, "re-requests... But, **but**, of course, weelll, let's see?" He backed up and peered into the main secured area of the jail. "Well it does look like you are in luck, the coast is clear, and, hum … Yes." He swirled around, his hand extended, "It is Julia Child, is it not?"

"Sure is," Julia grabbed his hand and pumped it. "I've never been in a jail before." Pretty soon, as the Sherriff ushered us through the security doors, Julia had him telling her about what they fed the inmates of the Pitken County jail for Sunday lunch, which he described with a sort of dazed look. She took it all in, and gave him some suggestions. And invited him to join her next year's picnic.

Cleared by security, we stood in front of Earl Biss's painted version of the Aspen grove at sunrise, which he captured for those incarcerated.

Awe brought silence.

"'Freedom'" I described how Earl, sometimes himself resident in the Pitkin County Jail, painted, in Crayola, on the block walls, a view of what, if they were free to walk out there, the inhabitants would be able to see. Freedom.

When we crossed the meadow back to the Jerome at twilight, Julia wiped her eyes, and hugged me. "Until we meet again. *Chère amie.*" She stood tall and hugged John Scharffenberger. "*Boutez!*" she called as she and John McJ. went into the hotel. Tomorrow we would all be "*en avant*" again, headed home.

John McJ and Julia were closer than ever as everyone could see. She relied on his shoulders, and his passion to continue the spark of enthusiasm so important to her *joie de vivre* and *amour-propre,* which she would need full measure of in the weeks and months ahead.

After this 1994 Salvation from Starvation Lunch, Julia returned to Cambridge to pick up her regular non-stop Summer schedule. She wrote me a few days after returning home that she was already looking forward to our next picnic-to-save-her-life: "Have I told you? I love fried chicken!"

I sent her a large bouquet of fresh herbs from my garden, knowing her Cambridge season was not yet producing in such quantity, and mine were abundant. She dried them and used them in *omelettes.* But before opening her doors to television crews and chefs and cables and air-conditioning lines snaking everywhere in her house, she personally answered every condolence on Paul's death. Then while battling pain of returning knee problems, she, with Stephanie Hersh, began to plan the new television series' PR tour, and the finishing of its companion cookbook. She and Geoffrey Drummond were a filming team, completing, she wrote, "the next shows for 'Master Chefs'." By mid-August, and her 82nd birthday, she, with Paul's family, reunited in Maine for a celebration of life, and spread his ashes. "Good bye to the old boy," she wrote. Then it was back to Cambridge, ever looking forward, to the writing of this new cookbook. *"Bouter!"*

Julia's knee was now so painful that during that October's tour of Florence she wrote she'd had to take pain medication. "I hate pills!" Pain-killers were better though, she reasoned, than further surgery, for which she just did not have time.

During that 1994 and 1995 winter while she continued her break-neck speed schedule of PR tours and writing on the book, we did meet in Santa Barbara a few times. While she continued her schedule in Cambridge and birthday celebration in Vinalhaven, Maine, the current companion cookbook, PR tours, and her continuing cooking stints in Venice, Italy, and at the Greenbriar, in Santa Barbara in September, during one tour, we met for lunch at Citronelle and carried our lunch conversation and unfinished bottle of wine back to her Seaview condo, and, over wine, she talked about new beginnings. By now you know her philosophy, no matter what: *en avant.* Forward!

Julia was, beyond all her business schedule, very involved with the American Institute of Wine and Food and its 1994 and 1995 current rejuvenation with Margrit Beaver and Robert Mondavi at their winery and at the new COPIA in Napa. One beautiful Fall afternoon I introduced Julia to a portraitist friend who, with a commission from Margrit Biever, did soon have Julia sit for a likeness on canvas, showing her in Seaview overlooking the ocean, This picture used to hang in (now closed) COPIA in Napa.

How do you capture a moonbeam?

Back on the road and back home in Cambridge and in Palm Springs that 1994 and 1995 winter we exchanged lots of notes and letters and faxes—(anyone out there remember that old waxed-paper stuff faxes were printed on?) Some of Julia's faxes have disappeared into yellow. But many delightful ones survive. And some of them are from December 1994 and January 1995. She liked the Yellow sunglasses I sent her to welcome in the New Year and a Champagne Christmas book, and promised we would meet again in Santa Barbara soon in the New Year 1995. (We had had an early December lunch.) And just in case her thank-you letters and notes for Christmas gifts and New Year's greetings did not convey her thanks sufficiently, she dashed off jolly cards with even more expressions of gratitude and express wishes that we get together again very soon. Julia loved giving thanks.

At the same time, not far away from her in Cambridge, John McJennett himself was sending me notes and letters, talking about the good progress he was making on the biography, saying he was enjoying RWB Lewis's on Edith Wharton. And happened to mention that he had sold his long-time New Hampshire house, adding that the packing up of his tools and manuscripts and clothes, furniture—("<u>after</u> the movers had left") had filled "2 panel trucks and 2 four-door vehicles"—of which one was Julia's large fire-engine red Volvo. Feeling liberated, he made more progress on his book on the New Hampshire Civil War Army surveyor who went out West to open the Northwest Territory. Taking Julia's suggestion for moving *en*

avant, and hired "a researcher to help dig up" the information he needed before "moving ahead to stage 2." He praises his darling Julia for finishing her latest companion cookbook for the Master Chefs. "She is truly a remarkable human being. We are both well—perhaps for me better than I deserve." He did not know that Julia was writing that John was "not doing so well." Contrary to what his lady-love said, he was "feeling just great," and, reenergized over "inspiration from the Edith Wharton biography." And doubtless inspiration from his lady love.

Perhaps Julia's worry over John's health was a psychological habit of worry about the man she loved. After fourteen years of daily concern over the state of Paul's declining health, the habit of worry is hard to forget, it seeps into the psyche and into the bones almost, possessing one. And maybe the worry was partly because she did see small signs that perhaps John's health really was not as great as he said.

At any rate, looking ahead with enthusiasm was another part of Julia's psyche, and she was. Notes arrived saying how much she was thinking of our Aspen picnics and wondering when we would get together. In March, 1995, I, because of a business trip to Champagne, was unable to join her at a fund-raiser. But, with John Scharffenberger, we offered Scharffenberger sparkling wine, and he attended the event. And Julia and I made plans to meet in Santa Barbara just prior to my departure over the Atlantic. We had lunch that March day in her condo, and talked until the sun was setting and I had to drive back to Palm Springs. She was in fine spirits, though confessing to missing Paul, and looked forward to seeing John soon. Remember what I have written? Julia loved men. Men made Julia come more alive, made her feel flirty, girly, sexy. And Julia loved all those feelings.

Aspen-time again! At last it was June 1995, and the fourth annual Save Julia Child From Starvation Picnic at the Jerome was about to begin. The cast of characters was arriving into this Silver-Lode town by stomach-tossing rides in little planes over the Rockies into the Pitkin County airport, or by vans from Denver, or via a wonderful interstate route through the mountains from Denver, passing buffalo grazing near Indian Chiefs' grave sites. I was John Scharffenberger's guest at his family's condo outside of Aspen. Julia and John McJennett were ensconced at the Jerome. We all met up Wednesday evening at the New Chefs' event, where two new chefs to whom I sold lots of Champagne in Los Angeles, Josiah Citrin and partner Raphael Lunetta, won the Aspen Food and Wine Best New Chefs competition. They were thrilled to meet Julia and have her taste their culinary creations. And Julia, surrounded by all these darling white coated young chefs was in paradise. We tasted and they traded recipes and techniques with Julia, and we all drank more Scharffenberger.

Julia had a particularly full Aspen schedule in 1995, doing her by now infamous demonstrations with Jacques Pepin. To the delight of the standing-room only house she trotted out wearing her larger than life Fire Chief's hat, carrying a huge fire extinguisher, pointing it at the dish Jacques was flambéing. The crowd went wild. Then Jacques added parsley to a dish they were preparing together and, when his back was turned, Julia tossed it in the trash. Howls of delight tipped Jacques off that Julia had tampered with his dish. And to top it all off Julia started melting pounds of butter for a hollandaise, whispering that she had to be *en garde*, constantly vigilant, lest the Food Police get wind of how much butter she used. She had them crying, holding their tummies in hysterics. That evening we all walked down the hill back to the Jerome together, Julia petting every cat she met along the way.

That Saturday night John Scharffenberger and I went to dinner not far from the Jerome, meeting up with wine-maker and chef friends who were excited about the next day's Saving picnic. After, as we sat in the Jerome's living room near the fireplace (Aspen gets quite cold in June after sunset) having chocolate cake and Scharffenberger *Rosé*—just to make sure both were up to par for the next day's picnic—, suddenly from over the backs of our well-padded chairs, we were greeted by an unmistakable voice. "Surprise! Surprise. 'Tis I. And John," Julia piped and came round to give us kisses and hugs. She and John McJ. had gone out for dinner too and were just returned. So we gathered more chairs and ordered more chocolate cake for further testing and more glasses of Scharffenberger. We were being regaled with Julia's jokes and stories about wonderful things, like shopping at E. Dehillerin and carving up a whole side of beef, when Eva Pekkala came by.

"Julia," I interrupted her, "have you met Eva? She's the Food and Beverage Director here." I knew Eva had never met Julia and was almost shaking in anticipation.

Julia reached out, pulled Eva over, and began questioning her. When she discovered Eva too was a graduate of Cornell's CIA, and in the class with her own Stephanie Hersh, Julia made sure Eva sat right next to her so they could get in a "good chat" about food and wine and hear what Eva liked. Julia gave of herself totally when it came to someone who wanted to know more about her special loves, classical cuisine, great wines, and butter. Out came more chocolate cake and more *Rosé* sparkling as the group expanded again, and then yet more again with other friends, and finally, with 'General' Tony DiLucia even more. I think by the time midnight rolled around we possibly had eaten all the chocolate cake new Executive Chef Todd had prepared. He too must have been quite surprised the next morning.

En route to Snowmass, John Scharffenberger was giggling.

"What's so funny?"

"Well, when I came back from paying the bill, passing the back elevators I almost stumbled upon Julia and John in a fierce embrace, his hands on—well you know—kissing so passionately they had no idea where they were and certainly none that I was a *voyeur.*"

We were happy *because* our Julia was happy.

Several times Julia had written: "I love fried chicken!"

Photo by M. Hill and K. Packer

Here is photographic proof of that pudding. This photo is taken just prior to most guests arriving to the 1995 picnic at the Hotel Jerome. There in full color is our goddess of cuisine, chatting with her new friend-in-food-and-wine, Eva Pekkala. And, while she's into the conversation, not missing a word, Julia's right arm is reaching out, snatching a piece of that chicken she so loved. Maybe she was remembering, with a kind of primordial fear, that Day of Enduring, that day with No Sustenance at Madeleine's; and was making sure that if by some horror the chicken disappeared, she would survive? Or maybe she was just being Julia, loving fried chicken?

The 1995 Save Julia Child From Starvation Picnic at the Hotel Jerome was in session, and the crowd exceeded all expectations, finally ending at 325 guests.

Photo of Julia with Hotel Jerome's Tony DiLucia by Steve Mundinger, Aspen Studios

Even Dana Cowin, Editor of Food and Wine Magazine, arrived with her entourage, joining all the regulars, and many new invitees. Naturally the Hazan family were there, this year with grandbaby.

Photo by Steve Mundinger, Aspen Studios

And after sabering, Jacques Pepin joined his buddies from Palm Springs for some laughs and fried chicken.

John McJennett, I noticed, different from the last three days when we'd met, was now accompanied by an oxygen tank. "The atmosphere was making me dizzy," he explained. Had Julia been perceptive? Maybe he was not as healthy as he made believe? At any rate the oxygen seemed to be working because, despite dragging it with him, John was full of fun, chatting up all the guests, old regulars and new-met friends.

After Julia's great-nephew Nikko and I served the first Scharffenberger sparkling wine, I found a place near John McJ. so we could have our talk about his book. "I'm stuck," he looked sad. "A vital piece of information which I need is missing. I cannot put my fingers on it; nor can my researcher. It's disappeared, probably with time or neglect. I don't think I'll be able to finish the book."

Well, I reasoned, if you are 82 and are feeling stuck, maybe someone should help get you unstuck so you can '*bouter.*'. "I don't want to intrude, but perhaps it's time you have that conversation with Dick Lewis? I am sure he could offer suggestions. Would you mind if I called him? Why don't I try to put us all together, getting your questions answered and you back on track?"

And like the goddess she was, Julia buzzed over, just in time to save the day. "I told you, I'd *love* to meet Mr. Lewis. His book on Florence you sent, and the Edith Wharton one, are wonderful. Let's get together." She was humming.

"This could be one of the times the Lewises are taking a sabbatical in Florence? I'll give a call when I get home. Not only would you both like to meet Dick, but Nancy Lewis, who is a wonderful cook, would adore to meet you, too."

"Oh, goodie," sang *La Julia.*

Having once more accomplished its goal, the 1995 Save Julia picnic was officially closed with the chocolate cake served by Nikko and me, and a grand round-the-Jerome-patio *carillon,* "bells of friendship" toast chimed by many glasses. During the course of the almost three hours of the picnic, it became evident that John McJennett's energy was being sapped by his difficulty getting enough oxygen. After hugs and some damp eyes, John Scharffenberger and I bid "until we meet again," to Julia and John and took off to hike in Maroon Bells. The gawking crowd at the front fence had disappeared; the city police had gone to supervise other events, the luncheon guests brushed crumbs from their laps and licked chocolate from their lips, and bid us and the Jerome bye-bye. Could the perfection of the 1995 Save Julia Child Picnic presaged the end of an epoch? Leave them laughing, if so. Julia's thank you letter sent from Cambridge on July 6 calls the picnic a "fixture of the Aspen experience! A great event!"

Maybe it's best to end something when it is at its ultimate expression? How to capture a moonbeam?

Capturing a Moonbeam
Julia and her real little family, Aspen 1995
Photo by Steve Mundinger, Aspen Studios

Chapter 5
Julia's Exciting Day Leads To Saving John's Book

I wasn't sure what I could arrange to save John's book, but I felt, knowing how adventurous the Lewises were, they too would enjoy this meeting, whenever, wherever it might happen. In July and August 1995, after phone calls back and forth between Palm Springs and Cambridge and New Haven, where the Lewises *were* in residence, we had a plan to save John McJennet's book. We were going to converge. In Cambridge. In August.

Julia was thrilled to meet Dick Lewis, "at last". But as usual she had "a schedule", busily filming the last of her newest series on Baking with Master Chefs. The last day of taping would be August 9.

And August 9 would be the moment of our convergence: we were invited to be Julia's guests to watch the final taping. The Lewises were eager. And so was I. Nancy and Dick trained in from New Haven, and I flew from LAX.

On the morning of August 9, I picked them up at the Harvard Club and drove us over to Irving Street. Dick Lewis also was accompanied by a pet oxygen tank on a leash.

He noted, as we walked up the street, that the house at 95 Irving had once been home to Henry James's brother, William. In 1991 Dick published a biography on the family, *The Jameses*. Obviously enjoying this trip, feeling the presences of lives he'd brought back to life in that narrative, he stopped next door, in front of 103. "This, then," Dick pointed, "was the house of Professor Josiah Royce. He and James often walked home together from The Yard, talking and discussing, after classes."

"Well, now it's Julia's house."

Who could have guessed? Dodging, side-stepping a tripping maze, I led them up to the front door, helping Dick get his metal dog over the clutter. The big house at 103 Irving Street was surrounded by vans spilling cables and film equipment, and trucks from which large aluminum slinky-tubes snaked into open doors, shooting air-conditioning throughout the proceedings, cooling a kitchen from baking-hot so cake-baking could happen. We were shown chairs in the rooms just off the kitchen. The real-time monitor gave us Julia and her Chef putting together that cake.

Don't we all have favorite Julia-stories about making cooking fun, how she specialized in mistakes? As though on cue, the Chef-du-Jour forgot to add espresso, so the proceedings had to stop, get rewound, and espresso found. Twirling about in her kitchen like a quail in search of lost chicks, Julia was in her element, humming her Song of the Pots, discovering the lost espresso and grabbing for a spoon. While the coffee got into the mix, her zany but precise running commentary got the laughs she gravitated to. Finally it was a "Wrap!" And Julia came out to meet and greet the Lewises.

A few weeks before, in late July, Julia faxed me that John McJennett's health had deteriorated and that he was moving into a retirement community where he would get needed attention.

She added that she was not sure he would be joining us.

While I felt certain that John would move heaven and earth to get together with Dick Lewis, not seeing him that morning at Julia's gave me a sinking feeling.

The show over, the air-conditioning people started scooping up their long aluminum tubes, and the film crew unplugged miles of cables. Stephanie ushered us outside to a pavilion set with lunch. With the crews and production staff and producer Geoffrey Drummond we had a convivial, talkative picnic in Julia's garden. Julia and Nancy Lewis gabbed cooking, Nancy's love and forte; Julia and Dick talked literature and teaching, which Julia loved, knowing she was a natural teacher. So she quizzed the Lewises and heard what they had to say about everything. She noted that Dick Lewis too had that companion he pulled along, his own canister dog, an oxygen tank, and commented that John, who would definitely join us for dinner the next night, also had such a pet.

Down by the River a symphony played: Convergence! Yes!

At 3 PM a last glass of wine was accepted and dessert came around family-style. Stephanie appeared from her office with a message for Julia; she handed a fax "from The Egg Board".

Julia sipped her wine and read the page twice. She put both glass and fax down, and looked at Stephanie. "This is serious stuff." She turned to the Lewises and me, called over Geoffrey Drummond, "The Egg Board has written to say there is an out-break of something called 'salmonella' which causes gastric problems, sometimes fatally, transmitted to us if we do not wash our hands after touching raw eggs and poultry. Who would have known? We all do it, all the time. But, as they point out, in the past eggs were safer because conditions between the egg and the consumer were much cleaner and quicker. Today with mass production these things occur easier." Julia looked at Stephanie and at Geoffrey Drummond, "Don't let the crew go; don't pack the film stuff. As soon as we finish lunch, I will go upstairs and script a program on this important issue. We will film this afternoon, and then decide when and where to air it." Geoffrey agreed. And Stephanie left to fax The Egg Board Julia's decision.

Soon thereafter Nancy and Dick and I hugged Julia at her front gate, leaving with promises to return by 5 PM the next evening.

And this goddess of cuisine, who had been up since 4 or 5 AM preparing her house and kitchen for the day's taping; who had studied the program's script down cold, who stood side-by-side in her crowded and not very cool kitchen, and, with a running commentary, assisted her Master Chef in his work in front of the camera and under hot spots for three or four hours; and who was, on that August 9, 1995, less than a week away from turning 83 years old, made the automatic decision to continue with this exciting day. Never did anyone to my knowledge ever hear Julia McWilliams Child complain of being "tired". Above all Julia loved to teach. By taking just another five or so hours—(she certainly was not counting)—, she could serve her profession and her fans. In typical Julia fashion, while we left to go to visit the Sackler museum at Harvard, she strode forward to continue her culinary work for all of us.

Chapter 6
Saving John Mc Jennett's Book
Convergence
Lift off

"First I believe that this nation should commit itself to achieving the goal, before this decade is out, of landing a man on the moon and returning him safely to the earth." John F. Kennedy to Congress, May 25, 1961.

Photo of John McJennett by the author

John McJennett was not a simple man. When I first met him in Aspen in 1993 he was accompanying his dear friend, Julia Child, to the "Food and Wine Classic". During that year's Save Julia Picnic, and during the next two, and through letters we exchanged, I got to know a little about this man who so stole *La Julia*'s heart. As I have written, if Julia palled about with him, he had to have quite a lot of brains. And brawn too. And, I add, a firm moral compass stuck permanently on Right. Our Julia was not one to equivocate about right and wrong. John McJennett had to be a smart and a good man.

Of which I got to learn more during our correspondence and conversations. One of these conversations was about his work in the 1960s and 1970s with NASA. I told him my daughter was working for NASA (designing the interior of the interplanetary Astronaut living quarters, 'Transhab'.) Hearing this he got quite excited. As he detailed about his years with NASA, I could picture him reporting on the Apollo Missions, being the person to coin the phrase, "successful failure", for the dramatic rescue of Apollo 13's crew. Indeed those missions he worked on shine like a beacon in the minds and hearts of all who worked for NASA, acting on our doomed Massachusetts President's request, symbolized today by the real presences of the Mercury-Redstone, Atlas and Titan, and Saturn V rockets themselves, standing tall and bright against the clear Florida skyline at Cape Kennedy, pointed toward the moon.

One night, while with Julia and John Scharffenberger, sitting in the lobby of Aspen's Hotel Jerome enjoying a last glass of the night, John McJennett talked a little about his Marine service when in Iwo Jima. But this is not what he loved talking about. He preferred discussing that "amazing woman, Julia" whom he knew he was so lucky to reconnect with at this stage of life.

Julia was humming, preening her legs, recognizing her own good fortune to have this Golden moment he gave her. She reached out and took his hand.

Over some of our Saving picnic lunches, or while walking up Aspen's sidewalks, John and I also discussed the Civil War surveyor who was brought out West in the 1880s by Nathaniel Banks to lay out the Western Territories for the US Government, about whom he was writing: the reason for our being together today in Cambridge, Massachusetts.

How it all came to be, on that muggy August afternoon, that we five were gathering at Julia's, actually started in the late 1930s, when Paul Child had a good friend who would become Mrs. John McJennett. Later, as John's wife, she and John reconnected with Paul and his wife, Julia, meeting through State Department activities in the 1950s, and again in the 1960s, through their work in the Foreign Service. The paths of John and Paul also crossed over a less pleasant experience, one caused by the trumped-up witch-hunt of Senator McCarthy in his House of Un-American Activities' trials. John McJennett strove, with his writing and intellectual skills, at creating saving rebuttals for those State Department members wrongly accused of Communist sympathy. Paul Child, himself in the State Department, was summarily summoned back to Washington, suspected briefly by the dreadfully misguided McCarthy henchmen.

Photo courtesy of the McJennett Family

1995, August 10, 5:15 PM, Nancy and Dick Lewis and I entered a transformed Child home, a mostly back-to-normal house. Except for a stray cable and a missing table, all was cleaned and polished. Somewhere for the next day's backup crew to find and replace was bound to be the missing teak kitchen table.

Waiting for us in the entrance was John McJennett. And though he had his oxygen-doggy with him, he put it aside most of the time. The man of the hour, with Julia at his side, was beaming. We introduced him to his idol, Dick Lewis and to Nancy. He took the Lewises into the living room to talk shop. I heard his opening salvos of 'How to get John over the Hump' of missing research information he felt he needed to complete his book. The door closed behind two cylindrical-oxygen pets.

In the kitchen Julia hummed about, ordering pots and skillets, and lids among her *batterie de cuisine,* while I prepared the *Rosé* Champagne she loved. Julia was in charge of the *hors d'oeuvres*: on tip-toe she reached for and retrieved her absolute favorite snack, Pepperidge Farm Goldfish, and poured generously from a huge box into a few bowls. Julia liked her Champagne from *coupe* glasses. She had some from Lalique which reminded me of Houseman's poem in which rose-lipt maidens dance for lightfoot lads. I found them dancing in the cupboard, and we sailed forth to meet the discussion. One of us popped the cork and poured frothy streams into five coupes, while the other passed goldfish. After ringing a "bells of friendship" *carillon* clink all around, and, bearing handsful of gold, Julia took Nancy and me to see Paul's paintings and some of his furniture.

Paul Child painted in stark contrast from his furniture. His furniture was more Renaissance in style, showing flourishing dexterity and talent for carving as well as design and expertise in massive construction. While I had seen many of Paul's charming and fanciful drawings for Julia's cookbooks, like the famous *batterie de cuisine*—the one shown on each of her letters and cards—his paintings were very different. While in earlier days he painted lyrically, and sometimes cubistically, of Venice's canals and Provence's fields, this un-lyrical style was modern to my eye, modern as was the 1930s and 40s mechanized stark-style, paintings dark and somewhat mysterious: still today I think of those paintings and would love to be able to talk to Paul about them to discover his dreams and inspirations, or despairs. Julia always said how much Paul and I would have gotten along: *comme toujours*, I agree with her. So, while we three girls talked and walked about, took more Champagne, and served some too, with their little tank-dogs at their sides, the men were deep into it, not noticing when we came and went through the living room. Finally, around 6:45, we poured the last of the two bottles of *Rosé*. Julia gave a last salute to her last drops and announced that the conversation would continue *en route* to dinner. "*Bouter!*"

Outside, Julia tossed me the keys, singing, "You drive, Madeleine."

We piled into her huge flame red Volvo. I say huge: it was Julia-sized; the driver's seat dwarfed me. I made adjustments and off we went. I did not back into her neighbor's car across the street, as Julia frequently did. I took us past Harvard Yard, down to Weeks Bridge, passing Dunster House, scene of fun times in my past, waving at the median-green filled with the elderly oaks, for which, in the 60s, we had patrolled as 'minute men', saving them from those mysterious who, who wanted to chop them down.

When I pulled into Storrow Drive and headed toward Boston I could see people in cars passing, on both sides, staring and gesturing oddly frantically. Julia started giggling. "They think the car is driving itself," she howled. "They can see four of us: Dick and Nancy and me" (they were in the back seat); She waved at one particularly curious carful, "they see John sitting up there in the front. But no one can see our driver. The 'Tale of The Headless Driver' has started!" Julia gulped air; she wiped tears of delight. She was correct. I was driving by looking through the steering wheel divisions; I was much too short for the Julia Flame.

The "headless driver" flaming vehicle pulled into Gordon and Fiona Hamersley's *Bistro* in Boston's South End. Julia loved not only the quality and seasonal diversity of the cuisine, but the talented owners too.

And she knew I had not seen Fiona or Gordon Hamersley since they married and left Los Angeles in the late 1980s. When I started in the wine business in Los Angeles one of my best customers was the wacky and delightful Fiona Leigh-Smith, Catering and Events Director for a hotel in West Los Angeles. Whenever we could we palled about meeting cute guys and enjoying good wine. At that very same time, on the other end of Los Angeles, in Hollywood, on Melrose, was a very cute, red-haired Assistant Chef to Wolfgang Puck at Ma Maison, Gordon Hamersley. One fate-decreed day the paths of these two crossed, and that was it: no more gadding about for Fiona. She fell in love with equally darling Gordon. Tonight I was going to see them again.

If I told you about all the dishes we enjoyed hat night, and described the wines and Champagnes we consumed, I would be making it up. Dinner was truly like a dream. Perfect. Perfectly delicious, perfectly happy. We talked and talked all together most of the time. The men solved John's book problems. Dick gave the perfect suggestions and even found an agent to represent John to get his work published. John was beaming. Possibly over a Jim Beam?—No, he was beaming over his favorite, Evan Williams.

His daughter, Linda McJannet, professor of Literature at Bentley University, joined us. Gordon came out to sit with us, and Fiona arrived after she bid goodnight to some guests. All together we talked until the wee hours, and the cows were leaving for the pasture. The night watchman cat arrived to say *bonjour* to Julia. And purring, we all piled into the Red Flame and headed back across The Charles. At that time of morning no one was out staring at the "headless driver". Converged contentment reigned.

Julia was never one to let grass grow under her feet. She was too busy striding forth, singing the Song of her Kitchen.

By the time I got home to Palm Springs there was a fax waiting from her. "*Chère Madeleine*: the big airconditioning (sic) tubes have gone home, as have all the crew. The cellar is bare, the dining table is back, the kitchen is almost in order, and all is so quiet! I miss everyone, and feel so fortunate to have been part of it, since we did have fun, and were like a big family. What a treat to end it all with that lovely evening so sweetly arranged by you. I loved the Lewises, and felt so at home with them after a bit of wining and dining. Sweet and nice people and much enjoyed by John. It did him good to come, and I'm glad you met his Linda—and she was delighted to meet Dick. How very sweet of you, *Chère Amie*, to arrange all of that! With love and many thanks—and *à bientôt j'espère*. Julia. PS we're having lovely weather today—clear and quite cool—Santa Barbara weather, as I always say to enfuriate (sic) the natives."

Here I offer you, in this Julia aria, a personal and important insight into the off-camera Julia Child. You see her pulling and pushing with and against any negatives. Can you picture, with me, Julia, somewhat melancholy, missing having a house full, much preferring all that mess to none at all? She even missed the noise and racket of the crew. Yes, *La Julia* threw herself into life with gusto. *Bouter!* Then, when the front door closed, and there was no noise, no confusion, when she was alone she was more than a wee-bit blue. This was not the first time she made reference to our meetings and gatherings being "like a family." You also glimpse, maybe to shoo away those blues, her puckish reverse to humor in her joke about the weather. After all it was August in Massachusetts, and, normally, extremely humid. Not at all like Santa Barbara's permanently clear skies and ever dry breezes.

Photo courtesy of the McJennett Family

Julia had written me before I left for Cambridge that John, "has not been in extremely good health, and is about to enter a retirement community where he can get some good attention if he needs it. He has a heart condition." But as swiftly, after my return, I was receiving John's letters, not corroborating all of what Julia's said, *comme toujours*. While he says he has indeed moved to a retirement home, which he calls, "The Velvet Warehouse", he is at this point just "settling in". He is most "positive" about Dick Lewis's suggestions and assistance toward his book's publication. And to that end he is getting the manuscript "cleaned up a bit" before sending it to Dick. John was also striding forward, excited about his life's possibilities.

Sometime in September Julia called and asked me to suggest.to her places to visit near, but outside, Venice. She was off like a rocket on her annual teaching stint at Venice's Cipriani Hotel.

Ancestors of mine founded Venice around 800 AD. I have visited some of the early cities from where they came, like Aquileia and ... "Grado," I replied to Julia. "Go to Grado. Best way to get there is by *motoscafo* from the front of San Marco, passing the Lido and out to Grado. But a car drive is gorgeous too, taking you in reverse from the drive in Hemingway's *"Farewell to Arms"*. First you pass Fossalta de Piave, then, with fishermen's huts dotting the horizon, on to Aquileia, founded by Julius Caesar, and finally to Grado, all the while on the Adriatic. Just to the north is Friuli, where great wines are made. And to the east, sitting on the border, is the cosmopolitan seat of the region, Trieste."

Julia chose the "Hemingway" drive. And soon I was getting cards from vineyards in Friuli, from Trieste, and finally one from Grado itself, where she said they had a delicious "fishy lunch. It's off-season now," she continued, "and quiet—and charming. We are enjoying this part of Italy. No American tourists." She finished by telling me that John had sent his manuscript off to Dick Lewis. Full Speed ahead! She PS'd that the Cipirani classes, always left her with hurting knees. Ah those striding knees! (If you look above at the photo of Julia and John with his family at Harvard commencement in June, 1995, you see Julia's hand rubbing that hurting knee; and John connected to his metal companion.)

By her return to Cambridge in November John was making strides himself, further developing his manuscript and enjoying renewed health in his "Velvet Warehouse' surroundings. Before setting off with him on a

Thanksgiving trip to celebrate with clan McJennett, Julia thanked me for a basket of "Lady Apples", which she had never had before, which she was taking to that gathering in Providence, at John's son's house, where daughter Linda and the whole family would also be. Julia and John were reveling in a passionate burst of young-love, thrilled in each other's company. And the company of a "real family" was the kind of gathering Julia craved; one with multi-generations, one of all sorts of occupations, conversations, and many ringing *carillon* toasts.

Julia with John F. McJennett III
Photo courtesy of the McJennett Family

1995 was the first December since I met Julia that she did not come West for Christmas, or that we did not meet somewhere for a holiday meal and glass, or two, of wine. She was in Cambridge making strides on that latest companion cook-book for the Baking Series, while John was toiling away making tracks on his Wild West manuscript. Both John and Julia were feeling renewed in body and spirit. It is possible that perhaps, though she was ever-practical, this time she wrote what she wished everything to be, just a little? Enjoying the gregarious company of her new family, she invited all the McJennett clan over for Christmas dinner at 103 Irving Street.

In January, 1996, John's health took a decided turn downward, which no wishing could change. When Julia sent me a copy of his obituary I knew she was at the utmost of distress because she dated the letter 1992. I'd learned that erratic dates on Julia's correspondence usually signified too much rushing about and/or hurting knees. But this time she was showing her heart's distress. Another sign was that she wrote me the same letter twice, saying how he had developed cancer which was "mercifully swift-acting".

On a day in late March, one which John's daughter Linda describes as being so pleasant and mild that they all walked over from the service at Harvard's Memorial Chapel, Julia opened her Cambridge house and heart to John's family and friends.

In Memoriam John McJennett, February 25, 1996.

Chapter 7
Oh Those Knees
The Art of Bouter

Julia McWilliams was vain about her long, glamorous legs, legs that swept her above other mortals, where, she said, the air was fresher, and the view clear. Julia was proud of those gams, especially when she could flash their bees-knees to be appreciated by that gallant, sexy, older man she'd set her sights on, Paul Child. Later Julia McWilliams Child was pleased to show off her magnificent stride when she performed in front of a live audience, or, for us all before a television crew. Daily she pranced about on those beauties God gave her: Julia was a strider.

But all that striding and standing, toiling over stoves and counters, took a pricey toll on her gams' knees. Beginning in the 1970s Julia had sought relief from doctors for the pain which seemed to grow, but to rarely diminish. Julia's predilection for action overrode doctors' prescriptions for "staying off the knees," or that other palliative they called, "time out." Julia was not a time-out girl. Relaxation for her was striding forward, even on painful knees, to learn more, meet more of us. So instead of relaxation and pain pills (she hated medicine), Julia resorted to the newly developed knee replacement surgery. She'd first heard about the condylar knee in France. In Boston she found this surgery was gaining more and more converts. So she had her first knee replacement surgery in the 1970s. By 1990 Julia had had more than four knee surgeries. But after closing *la Peetch* in 1992, after Paul's declining health in 1993 and subsequent death in 1994, and then after John's illness and death in 1996, Julia came face-to-face with a lot to organize and personally accomplish. With no time for long recuperation that orthopedic surgeons always counseled, she had to grin and bear the knee pain.

In November 1996, when she wrote from Cambridge inviting me for our usual Christmas meal and Champagne upon her arrival in Santa Barbara in December, she had something important to discuss. She gave me a different address in the same complex because her Seaview condo was on the market, and she was borrowing another. In Julia-style, she advised me not to bring any "eatments" because she had plenty.

Iced Champagne was very acceptable for me to arrive with. Almost as popular with our goddess of cuisine as those Golden Pepperidge Farm fish, was *Braunschweiger et fils* Norwegian-style *leverpaste,* a rich and delicious *pâté*-like concoction. 'Yum-yum," Julia cut slices and served it with rye bread. We chimed a *carillon* with the Rosé Champagne. And when she sat facing me she seemed, for the first time to my eyes, a little less energetic. Well, hello? Julia had just gotten off a five-hour flight across the U.S., capping off months of striding around on PR tours, teaching at the Greenbrier, receiving awards here and there, signing books for Planned Parenthood, and attending fund-raisers for the American Institute of Wine and Food.

But there was more to her less energetic expression.

She cleared her throat, took another swallow of Champagne and a bite out of a *canapé* of *pâté.* "I'm making the move," she began. "Not far from here. Lovely condominiums; each with a separate garden and patio. I can be as independent as I wish, just like here, or on Irving Street." She took more Champagne, and more *pâté.* She stood up and walked a bit and showed me a copy of her newest book which she had been signing at Planned Parenthood fund-raisers. Sitting again, she did not resume. This was not an easy conversation for Julia to have. She had thought and thought about this.

She knew this was the right thing to do. But as she described, I saw the mental adjustments, her picturing the many changes. And those were not coming easily. Julia was a free bird, used to independently striding through the world, teaching and learning and enjoying. Heretofore her courageous behavior was bolstered by masculine companionship and support with business arrangements and households. Now she was looking at big changes from the solo perspective and at her own mortality. It reflected in her eyes. The pause was extended.

Then I realized that Julia was asking. Asking me to give her my opinion of what I thought of her decision to sell the lovely Seaview condo, and to move into—whatever phrases one prefers to call Casa Dorinda—a retirement facility.

So, we had more *Champagne*, and she made more *hors d'oeuvres*, and we settled back to talk through the steps. She would keep Irving Street, "for now", because she had tons of work to do in the East: television shows she'd not yet dreamed up; companion books to write, and PR tours that originated from that side of the country. There where she had her families: both the Child family and the Clan McJennett. She had no intention of not keeping up that familiar schedule.

"You are," I suggested, "putting your ducks in a row. Re-organizing, cutting, prioritizing to that which you prefer and most enjoy doing. You already see how this move will allow you, not less, but more independence." She looked hard at me at that. "Access to dinner, for example, if indeed you should arrive late after a long trip and find your refrigerator to be Madeleine-bare. At Casa Dorinda you will not starve."

"Like today." She chortled and finished her glass. "I knew my plane would be late, and you were coming. I had to scramble and call ahead to get these things delivered." She cut more *Braunschweiger pâté* and spread a few rye bread slices. "You are right. If Paul and I arrived late at *La Pitchoune*, Simca made sure the refrigerator was full. My schedule is not getting lighter, *chérie*. Those little niceties are indeed what I want."

"Access to more neighbors, if you need a cup of sugar?" She laughed. "Access to telephone switch-board service which is always good, especially with the volume of calls you get, Julia."

She poured more Champagne. Now she was looking more like Julia: confident. She began to catch me up on her last year, describing wineries she'd visited in Friuli, and more about the "fishy meal" she'd enjoyed in Grado. Finally, her mind more settled, she talked about John McJennett's courage during his last weeks; about how much she appreciated his family; how supportive and embracing of her they were.

But then, attempting to get up, she audibly flexed her knee. We both winced; that noise had to have hurt. She stood erect and matter-of-factly said that "soon" she would have to have some surgery, and that, for "recuperation" Casa Dorinda afforded more in care.

"This is where I grew up," she gestured toward the dark Ocean, "right by the Biltmore we spent summers. My youth is out there." Maybe she was also picturing sitting in the sun on her new patio, away from the snow and ice of Cambridge, writing, as she had done all those past winters in *La Peetch*? She still had many friends in Santa Barbara and in nearby Pasadena, friends from those golden, youthful days in the area. As she talked, she gained back her sparkle, her looking forward to Next. From hesitancy, Julia stood even taller, discovering that Santa Barbara would be a fountain of youth, her new place in the light.

By the time I got home a loving fax, mostly in French, was waiting, thanking me, "with love from Julie."

Indeed in 1997 she did sell the Seaview condominium, and did move into Casa Dorinda. Often between 1997 and 1999 we met there for meals, religiously around holidays, and for drinks and talks. Julia liked movies, so we went to movies. We gabbed, dreaming about creating a fund-raiser for the AIWF in Palm Springs, a Julia Child Golf Tournament: she would ride on a cart—"Alas, I can no longer walk a golf-course"—, from tee to tee passing out iced Champagne and taking "a turn now and then at a swing."

By 1999, with the security Casa Dorinda gave her, buoyed by Pacific sea-breezes, she approved an increased PR touring schedule, "trotting about" with Jacques Pepin promoting their new TV-series, *Julia and Jacques Cooking at Home*. Because of the renewed "trotting", coupled with continuing her bi-coastal living—Julia determined it was "time", and announced in late 1999 that she simply *had* to have that knee replaced.

Those knees were hampering the free-style she had created for her own enjoyment as well as ours, her adoring fans. "Soon," she would do it.

Soon.

In March of 2000, while she had to decline my invite to the Santa Barbara Film Festival *("Flûte!")* to meet Antony Hopkins because she'd just had a "one day medical adventure with no after effects", in the same breathe she invited me over to her place before The Festival to have tea and sherry. On the day, when she opened the door, she was *again* using a cane.

"I finally did it!"

Back in Cambridge, in October she wrote, "my knee is doing just fine; I am pleased indeed that I finally did it! See you in December!"

From then on I find it hard to keep up with the number of knee replacements and surgeries Julia had. *Flûte!* Darn those bees-knees. But once Julia did something, with no complaints she touted its benefits. Indeed, when we did meet at Christmas 2000, Julia, on her own, without any cane, was the image of a renewed *Marianne Marseillaise* battling for our culinary happiness. The knee replacement was a success!

Julia Child's Kitchen is closed and sent to the Smithsonian Museum.
Photo courtesy of Stephanie Hersh

The Cambridge house was sold; and the kitchen packed up and sent to the Smithstonian and Julia was a full time resident of the Wild West.

For March 2001 Julia and I scheduled a gala outing to the Santa Barbara Film Festival, which that year was honoring Diane Keaton with the "Modern Master" award.

Julia coming to the Santa Barbara Film Festival with her niece, Rachel and the author

And rumor had it the presentation was to be done by none other than Steve Martin. Julia enjoyed tremendously their films, and, admired the work of both stars beyond their acting talents, as directors and musicians.

In her delight, she decided "To get all dolled up".

And, all dolled up, *La Julia* opened the door.

But, *flûte!* Again, that darn cane was in her hand, a necessary accoutrement to her elegant *robe du soir* ! Obviously that knee was not all it was trumpeted to be. But far be it from Julia to say anything negative.

Because my guest was Julia Child, I, as a sponsor of the Festival, arranged for the Theatre auditorium to be made available to us for early entry, before the jostling crowds. Exiting from the limousine, Julia accepted my arm up, and together we walked the Red Carpet at a slower-than-Julia pace. Like a sudden small breeze picking up into a whirlwind, a few in the large group on the other side of the velvet rope began with whispers, "Julia Child?"; "It's Julia Child?" Then came calling out down the line, "it is Julia Child." Until finally the throng was shouting, "HELLO, JULIA!"

And like the magician's wand, those cheers erased knee pain and, like an abracadabra, had Julia waving and smiling and calling back, "hello to you!" Though the rest of the walk was surely not painless, she stood taller and walked with less use of the cane. Julia had fans to entertain, and, like the star she was, she did.

At dinner after no one would have suspected the knee was hurting.

At the gala dinner after, Julia was seated with the Santa Barbara sponsors of the evening's events. Almost back-to-back with Julia was Diane Keaton, at whose table I was. When I asked Diane if she would like to meet Julia Child, she put down her fork, "Oh, yes," she said as she pushed back her chair, and began to stand while finishing with, "Of course." Diane looked as though I had asked her if she wished to meet God.

When I whispered in Julia's ear that Diane Keaton was there to meet her, she put down *her* fork, *"Bien sûr,"* as she stood she spoke, and holding out her hand, "Hello, I'm Julia Child, congratulations, Diane."

Diane Keaton approaching Julia Child.

These two shots I snapped show the wonder Diane Keaton felt as she did meet the 'goddess' of cuisine and a fellow great performer. Also you see Julia's natural delight in talking with those from whom she could learn more.

Julia chatting up Diane.

Julia Child's rallying cry, *"Bouter en Advant"*, 'Forward, Full Steam Ahead", was Julia's preferred gear.

Just when all Julia's ducks were in a row, just when Julia was most positive, when she was no longer responsible for property up-keep, when nothing else could possibly hamper her from resuming her full speed ahead stride, just when she was preparing to *Bouter* anew, those knees, those once gorgeous bees knees did it, sending her into a spiral. A whirlpool.

I'd sent Julia a New Year's card of a beautiful mermaid swimming. Julia wrote back how much it suited her, remembering how she'd been such a good swimmer.

Unfortunately, sometimes situations cause "regress full speed ahead."

In May, 2002, I offered Champagne support for a Santa Barbara-area organization to which Julia was committed, "Direct Relief". The event was at the Santa Barbara Yacht Club.

Her eyes were sparkling; her smile was happy but quizzical: Julia was walking toward me, but she was not walking. She was pushing herself along with a "walker". While she was happy to see me, in her eyes I could see her dismay, wondering what all those fans surrounding her might be thinking, seeing her so infirm, seeing the change from Julia standing tall, clanking pots and pans and flipping *omelettes;* seeing her so different from the "Bon Appétit!" warbler. That darn knee was not just acting up again, it was being downright dangerously painful. Nevertheless, on came Julia. There was nothing I could do but to take her arm and walk slowly with her, chatting, to the table where she would, for almost two hours, sit, signing her latest book, offering the proceeds to "Direct Relief."

"You know the drill, *chérie,*" she looked at me, a smile in her eyes, her shoulders hunched slightly, but her voice strong. Her knee was hurting, that too was in her eyes and in the pressure her fingers exerted on my arm as she sat.

Yes, I did know Julia's book-signing "drill". With a bunch of Post-Its, I went down the long line of supporters wanting their books signed by Julia, explaining that each should print clearly any salutation they wished Julia to write, along with their name as legible as possible. The long column began to inch forward, and she autographed book after book, chatting a word with each.

While she continued, those whose books were done were seated in back of us, *a table,* enjoying lunch, washing down the *délices du chef* with the Champagne I had offered. I brought over glasses and small plates. We clinked. "Thank you, *chérie.* I am hungry." Yes, I, the friend who had once starved Julia, knew well that *La Julia* needed to eat. She sipped, she signed, she tasted, she signed, she sipped…and on it went until she could put away her pen, and, actually. *a table* herself, enjoy the *Plat Principal.* "*Pas mal de tout,*" she wiped her lips and finished her Champagne. It had been a good lunch, and, renewed, she took her walker and went to greet more of the guests. Slowly, but forward, she progressed.

Shortly after that day in May 2002, that bad knee was re-replaced. Not many months after, an invitation of mine for an excursion to see the new Bacara spa–hotel-restaurant complex, which I knew she was eager to explore, was declined because that "20-year-old knee replacement has gone bad. It will be several more weeks before I am up and about again. Alas."

Alas, it was more than a few more weeks before she was up and about.

Oh, those knees. Yes, that knee had "gone bad" again. From the pain she had no relief. So, in September 2002, the re-re-replacement took place. With any surgery the unexpected can arise. With this one Julia experienced serious complications. A bad reaction to penicillin meant that this replacement had to be removed so her empty socket could cure and heal before a new implant could be inserted. After weeks in the hospital, without a knee, flat on her back, Julia was removed to a recovery center for recuperation and therapy. It is hard to picture the tall, robust goddess of our kitchens, our *cuisine* revolutionary, Julia *Marianne Marseillaise*, as anything else than vibrantly striding ahead. But those knees had stopped her in her tracks. Instead of striding, Julia was forced into the opposite. With no knee in that leg, Julia could not stand, could not walk.

After all the surgeries it was difficult to get back her vibrancy. She saw in herself some of what she had experienced when Paul and when John were ill. Those visions she now worked hard to reverse and to conquer. But days of feeding tubes and total care in hospital takes its toll on the youngest of us. Julia, whom I once had starved, who loved to dine, had to undergo weeks of speech therapy and eating therapy to re-learn to eat and swallow properly, and to speak normally. Well, not exactly 'normally': Julia had therapy to relearn to speak like Julia. Just when she thought she was getting her strength back, another or another set-back would occur. But Julia had gumption, and she persisted. Besides she had her great facilitator in this recuperation: her always capable, Stephanie Hersh.

Not long before Stephanie had moved out to Santa Barbara where Julia really needed her. Stephanie, with her training at Cornell's Culinary Institute of America, was shocked by the lack of quality in the meals served Julia and her fellow inmates in recuperation. End of November, 2002, Stephanie sent out emails proselytizing for better nutrition and attention to quality of preparation and in taste for meals for the recuperating infirm. She could see the difference in Julia when Julia got a delivery of In-And-Out Burgers vs. the meals "dropped off in an unmarked van". With tasteless food at the recuperation center, Julia lost an alarming amount of weight. As related, I sent boxes of Pepperidge Farm Goldfish and large bars of Scharffen Berger chocolate. Added to that, with the ice-cream and peanut butter Stephanie brought in, Stephanie wrote that Julia had gained "five pounds."

Then "Adventure" gave Julia a big boost.

In December 2002, Julia got a real lift in her effort to overcome:

A "crane thing", Stephanie wrote, lifted Julia, swinging her up and into the swimming pool for movement therapy. Julia relished the freedom the water gave her, making "like a mermaid". Stephanie likens the crane to the *Toy Story* "claw", and wrote, thanking for gifts and phone calls, saying how "the therapists are impressed with Julia's determination and her progress." Who would have thought Julia could be anything less than "impressive"; do anything other than make "progress"? Julia was on her back, but she was still demonstrating *"Bouter en Avant!"* Though the steam was less than full, the engine was getting back into striding form.

While Julia was a realist, there were things she preferred to view through her special lens. Like how much one could accomplish. 2003 and 2004 found Julia working on getting stronger. She was taking things, from necessity caused by those overwhelming physical adversities, a little slower.

Somewhere out in Long Island City a blogger was carping and crying into her Boeuf Bourguignon that Julia had snubbed her, ignoring her not-exactly proffered invitation to dinner.

But Julia had been permanently kneed-out of coast-to-coast PR touring; there'd be no new TV-series creating, which she so loved. However, with her Johanna Factotum at her side, she was, despite daily struggles, beginning to *bouter* back. She recharged and found renewed spirit. Again she heard the Song of the Kitchen as in her younger days, reviving her love of cooking. With Stephanie as *sous-chef,* Julia was relearning the notes of her special Song where she moved to the joyous sound of pots clashing, and of steam rising, swaying to aromas of perfectly poached fish, which the saucepan of flavorsome *beurre blanc* awaited, toe-tapping in anticipation of the cognac-scented duck *pâté.*

As much as her "Roo de Loo" Paris kitchen, she was now enjoying her little Casa Dorinda kitchen, where she'd even had the walls opened up a "Wowza" three inches so Wolfgang Puck could shoot a program, cooking with Julia. And, at the end of those sunny, pleasantly long days, she retired with her new kitty at her side, to dream of completing more of her Song of the pots and pans, to be banged out on her *batterie de cuisine,* the very next day.

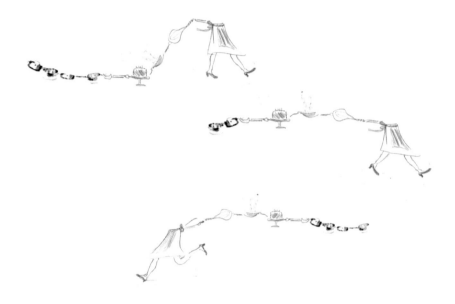

During the Summer of 2003 Julia was, though frail and using a walker for a while, graduated to her silver-topped cane, and was making bigger strides ahead. In her personal life she had the pleasure of knowing her kitchen from the Cambridge house would be around for new generations to see and learn about her cuisine revolution because it had been moved, "lock, stock, and *fouet*" to Washington, D.C.'s Smithsonian, American History Museum. At the same time, she was putting many of her papers in order, preparing to write her next book, one she completed dictating to her writer-nephew, Alex Prud'homme, on August 12, 2004.

And in ten more hours I would nestle a magnum of *Rosé* Champagne into ice, preparing to make a surprise trip for Julia's birthday, a trip I would never take on August 13, 2004.

EPILOGUE

I believe that at the end of their day, when the Curators at the Smithsonian go home, and the lights are dimmed in "Julia's Kitchen", then, in the dead of night, begins that Song with which Julia imbued those cabinets and table and *batterie de cuisine* during all the years when they served her well while she cooked for us all; during the vast night when the cats prow, Julia's pots clang and steam rises from the E. Dehillerin fish poacher, the duck *pâté* infused with cognac arranges itself on the platter Julia loved to serve it on, the sounds of Champagne corks popping reverberate, and her special rose-lipt dancing nymph coupe Champagne glasses wait to be filled when the guests arrive.

And there she is in the spotlight: Julia herself, our *Marianne Marseillaise.*

She stands in the door, her apron string hung with a towel for any slight mistakes, and in her hand she waves her *fouet:*

"Entrez, entrez tous, mes chers amis. Bienvenue; welcome all to my kitchen. This is Julia Child: *bon appétit!"*

Julia Child with the Big Fouet photo by Bonnie Schiffman

Photo courtesy of Stephanie Hersh

Photo courtesy of Stephanie Hersh

THE END.

ACKNOWLEDGMENTS

If Credits is a page giving credit, Acknowledgements is a page giving Thanks. So many friends, old and new, contributed in special, sometimes unexpected ways, to this book.

Agnes Jones, my long-time friend from Champagne, kindly read the manuscript and, beyond duty, gave me all the French accents I could not remember. Then she took it upon herself to give me more background on Julia's generating cry, *Bouter en Avant!* What a friend!

To Stephanie Hersh, who sent me some of the most enthusiastic and poignant photos of her mentor, Julia, I send heartfelt thanks.

Los Angeles-based professional photographer, Bonnie Schiffman, with great charm, and to my delight, gave permission to use her iconic image of Julia and The Big Fouet. From the cover to the Epilogue her photograph has informed the theme of my *mémoire*.

Steve Himes of Telemachus Press has not left my side in going through the manuscript, making suggestions, most of which I did follow. In fact when I have trouble, and wonder if this or that should be in the story, I now think first of what Steve might say before making a choice.

Johnny Breeze, graphic artist of Telemachus Press, is a true genius. Somehow Johnny knows before I do what it is I would like to see. Next time I think I shall just let Johnny do the graphics without telling him one word.

Diana Carey of Harvard's Schlesinger Library, kindly and promptly sent me links and information about the Julia and Paul Child collection of photographs. She made my work so easy in choosing a photograph to show exactly what Julia and Paul must have cherished most about their *Provençal* home, *La Pitchoune.*

Denise Faïfe, of the research department of Paris's *Musée d'Orsay,* also was like an angel, quickly appearing out of the Internet and flying to fix my quandary of how to get permission to reproduce paintings the Museums of Paris own.

Belinda Oster, Assistant to Tony DiLucia, General Manager of Aspen's Hotel Jerome, dragged her boss outside the hotel and took the photo I use of Tony.

The John F. McJennett family, daughter Linda and niece Gretchen, immediately replied, sending precious photos of John McJennett and Julia which beautifully filled-in needed gaps.

Palm Springs friend, Adam Zack, swiftly consigned to the USPS his prized photo taken with Julia here at my house.

And equally, friends Kevin Packer and Michael Hill did likewise, searching in their files to find and send photos they took of Julia and us all at some of my picnics for Julia in Aspen at Hotel Jerome.

Professional photographer, Steve Mundinger, of Aspen Studios, during his busiest season, searched days in *his* archives and found appropriate photos he too took of Julia and us all at those picnics.

Again, close to home, in Pomona, California, is The Collins College of Hospitality Management, which presented *La Julia* with an honorary degree.

Dean Lea Dopson and Chef Briones and their staff of Chefs and teachers, and Lisa McPheron, Director of Communications, came together pronto and gave permission to use the photo Julia sent me from that special award presentation day.

The Julia Child Foundation for Gastronomy and the Culinary Arts gave me permission to reproduce of one of the many letters send to me by Julia.

A book is far more than a collection of words. Pictures **are** worth thousands of them. And friends are invaluable. To each and all: *grands bisous*—lots of kisses.

Finally I, imitating Julia, call out to each of you with her admonition: *Boutez en Avant!* Full Speed Ahead! each and all.

Image Credits in Order of Appearance

Johnny Breeze, Telemachus Press: creator of the cover with photo from Bonnie Schiffman.

Agnes Jones, my chère amie from Reims, Champagne, for offering the grammatical-graphics of French accents throughout the manuscript.

The *Musée d'Orsay*, Paris, and *Denise Faïfe*, Service recherche: permission granted to reproduce images of the painting of Eugène Delacroix, "Le 28 Juillet; la Liberté guidant le people, 1830, Musée de Louvre, acquis au Salon de 1831. (la Liberté is referred to throughout the story as Marianne Marseillaise.)

Bonnie Schiffman, photographer: permission for reproduction of her iconic photo of Julia and the Big Fouet.

Cal Poly, Pomona, California, The Collins College of Hospitality Management, Dean Lea Dopson and Chefs, and Lisa McPheron, Director of Communication: permission granted for photo of Julia with Chefs at Julia's doctorate award ceremony.

Adam Zack: permission for reproduction of photo of him with Julia at my house.

The Julia Child Foundation for Gastronomy and the Culinary Arts: permission granted for reproduction of one of Julia's letters to me with The Julia Child Foundation's logo.

Tony DiLucia, General Manager Hotel Jerome, Aspen, and Belinda Oster, Assistant to Tony: for the photograph of Tony in front of the Hotel Jerome.

The *Musée d'Orsay*, Paris, and *Denise Faïfe*: permission granted for reproduction of their painting of Edouard Manet's, Le déjeuner sur l'herbe, 1863, donation d'Etienne Moreau-Nélaton en 1906.

Michael Hill and Kevin Packer: permission for reproduction of photos from Save Julia picnics in Aspen: of Julia enjoying the Scharffenberger, of Julia clapping, of "a real little family", of "my yellow hat", of Julia and John McJennett and John Scharffenberger, and of Julia sneaking fried chicken, from various years.

Steve Mundinger, photographic studio, Aspen: permission for reproduction of his photos taken at Save Julia: of Julia savoring the Rose, of Julia with kneeling Harley Baldwin and me, etc, of Jacques Pepin sabering, from various years.

Photo of the Chocolate Cake from Save Julia Picnics, Aspen, courtesy of the author.

The Schlesinger Library, Radcliffe Institute, Harvard University and Diana Carey: permission to reproduce Paul Child's photo of the Child's home in Provence, La Pitchoune.

The *Musée d'Orsay*, Paris, and *Denise Faïfe*: permission for reproduction of Claude Monet's, Le déjeuner sur l'herbe, entre 1865 et 1866, accepté par l'Etat à titre de dation en paiement de droits de succession pour les musées nationaux en 1987.

The author: photo of Phila Cousins and son Nikko.

The John F. McJennett family and Gretchen S. Coffman: permission to reproduce photos: of John McJennett hugging Julia in yellow blouse, of Julia and John at Harvard, of Julia with John F. McJennett III.

iStock Photo Copyrighted images: Chef's Hat 17297089/RTimages; Little Copper Pots 20236742/verdateo; Hearts: 1222473/lunagraphica; Kisses: 34963852/MihailUlianikov; Rocket Launch:18769121/TheRoff97

The author: photos from The Santa Barbara Film Festival honoring Diane Keaton, 2001: of Julia and Rachel Child and the author in limousine, of us at the Theatre Presentation, of Julia at dinner with Festival Sponsors, of Diane Keaton meeting Julia, of Julia chatting with Diane Keaton.

Stephanie Hersh: for permission to use her photo of Julia and herself at the time of the closing of the house, the iconic kitchen and their office at 103 Irving Street, Cambridge, Mass.

And, Steve Himes, Telemachus Press: for work on all graphics, photographs and editing throughout the manuscript.

ABOUT THE AUTHOR

Bouter En Avant! Full Speed Ahead with JULIA CHILD, is Madeleine's first venture into biographical *memoire* storytelling. Her first novel, *The Night Julius Caesar Invented Champagne*, is an adventure to the first vine and a history of high civilization according to the god Dionysos. Currently she is finishing her fourth stage play and researching the sequel to *The Night Julius Caesar*.

Visit the author website:
http://www.madeleinedeJean.com

Or read the Madeleine's blog:
http://champagnetoujours.blogspot.com

Made in the USA
San Bernardino, CA
20 March 2019